MEMOIRS
of a
CAPE BRETON
DOCTOR

Dr. C. Lamont MacMillan

NIMBUS
PUBLISHING

Nimbus Publishing Limited
PO Box 9166, Halifax, NS B3K 5M8
(902) 455-4286 nimbus.ca

Printed and bound in Canada
Cover design: Heather Bryan

Library and Archives Canada Cataloguing in Publication

MacMillan, C. Lamont (Carleton Lamont), 1903-1978
Memoirs of a Cape Breton doctor / C. Lamont MacMillan.
ISBN 978-1-55109-757-2

1. MacMillan, C. Lamont (Carleton Lamont), 1903-1978.
2. Physicians—Nova Scotia—Cape Breton Island—Biography.
I. Title.

R464.M27A3 2010   610.92   C2009-907327-7

The Canada Council | Le Conseil des Arts
for the Arts | du Canada

NOVA SCOTIA
Tourism, Culture and Heritage

We acknowledge the financial support of the Government of Canada through the Book Publishing Industry Development Program (BPIDP) and the Canada Council, and of the Province of Nova Scotia through the Department of Tourism, Culture and Heritage for our publishing activities.

This book was printed on
Ancient-Forest Friendly paper

ANCIENT FOREST
FRIENDLY™

CONTENTS

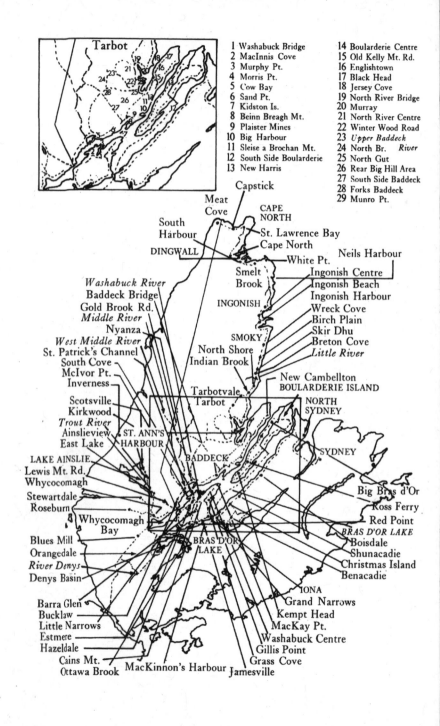

1 Washabuck Bridge	14 Boularderie Centre
2 MacInnis Cove	15 Old Kelly Mt. Rd.
3 Murphy Pt.	16 Englishtown
4 Morris Pt.	17 Black Head
5 Cow Bay	18 Jersey Cove
6 Sand Pt.	19 North River Bridge
7 Kidston Is.	20 Murray
8 Beinn Breagh Mt.	21 North River Centre
9 Plaister Mines	22 Winter Wood Road
10 Big Harbour	23 *Upper Baddeck*
11 Sleise a Brochan Mt.	24 North Br. *River*
12 South Side Boularderie	25 North Gut
13 New Harris	26 Rear Big Hill Area
	27 South Side Baddeck
	28 Forks Baddeck
	29 Munro Pt.

PREFACE

*M*any years ago I was hunting in the Rear Big Hill area of Cape Breton. Before the turn of the century, this area had been heavily populated. By the time I opened my practice in Baddeck in 1928 there were only three families living there. Now there is no one.

While walking through the woods, I found myself in an area so thick with underbrush I had to get down on my hands and knees and crawl, pushing my gun ahead of me. Suddenly I realized that I was in an old burial ground, with tombstones all around me. Here was all that remained of a once flourishing community. Each tombstone told its story. Many marked the last resting places of children and young adults. As I read the names and ages at time of death, I conjured up in my mind pictures of the homes where those people lived, the suffering they had endured, the helpless anguish of their families. I found myself wondering, "What was the cause of death? Did these young people have any medical care? Could a doctor have helped them?"

I wondered, too, about the doctors who had served the early settlers. During my own practice I encountered many of the same difficulties those early doctors must have faced. Often the most difficult part of my work was reaching the patient in the back country. Today Cape Breton has fine modern roads, and even the secondary roads are kept plowed in the winter. But as recently as twenty years ago I answered winter calls by horse and sleigh, snowshoes, or on foot across frozen lakes or bays.

Those early doctors must have been rugged men indeed. Unfortunately, little is known about them. I can understand why they left no records. When a single call may involve miles of travel by horse or on foot and take several days, there just isn't time to keep a journal.

I left this pioneer graveyard very saddened, but I realized, too, that most pioneer graveyards told the same story.

Some of the old-timers had stories of the doctors who preceded me. I've collected all the information I could find about these early doctors, both from official records in the Nova Scotia Archives and from the "oral history" of this region, the stories passed down from one generation to another. Their story is an important part of our heritage and deserves to be preserved for future generations.

I want to thank all of my friends of Victoria County who have shared their memories with me to make possible this reconstruction of a way of life. Being a busy country doctor for so many years didn't prepare me for scholarly biography. If I have done this well, it is because of the unselfish aid given me by my friends. I acknowledge the help from Mr. Sydney Maslem when this narrative was taking form. I thank Mrs. Pamela Newton for her advice during that difficult period when I was cutting the book down to an acceptable size. Finally my thanks go to Mrs. Dorothy Holman for her help in bringing the book to its final form before it went to the publisher.

INTRODUCTION

The year 1784 saw the Island of Cape Breton separate politically from the mainland of Nova Scotia and become a new province. Grants of land were available to new settlers as never before, and many immigrants, deported from the highlands and islands of Scotland, took advantage of them. For the most part, these new citizens settled in rural Cape Breton. When they landed, their possessions were very few, their sufferings and privations unimaginable. Physically and psychologically they suffered for want of adequate medical services—there were none except in the Sydney and Arichat areas, and with transportation as it was then, Sydney and Arichat were a long way from all rural communities. Those of us who have visited a pioneer cemetery are saddened by the death of so many young people. I always wondered how many could have been saved to live out a normal span of life if they had had medical services. But rural Cape Breton saw many years without trained medical personnel.

The Clergy, especially the Presbyterian ministers sent out from Scotland as missionaries, had studied some principles of medicine during their college course. They regarded it as part of their ministerial duties to attend to the health of the people entrusted to their spiritual care. It was as important to ask about the Epsom salts, sulphur and molasses as it was to answer correctly, "What is effectual calling?" But these clergymen also probed deeply into the moral nature of their flock. And this attention to virtue, I have no doubt, produced results that made for "the inculcation of those virtuous habits that redound to the health of the individual."

Traveling on horseback, winter and summer, along primitive paths in the forests, these ministers let nothing deter them from their monthly visits. The late Frank McGregor of Nyanza had a story about those early years, when all homes in the country had a spare bedroom downstairs that was always ready for any guest, especially the minister on his monthly call. It was the custom in winter to send the maid to that bed early in the evening to warm the bed. When bedtime came, the hostess would awaken the maid and send her to her own room. In those times the Scottish clergy were not against a little good Scotch whisky on a cold winter night just before bed. On one occasion the wee drop must have been repeated, because the hostess forgot to wake the maid. The minister was given his candle, and he started for the spare bedroom. When he opened the door and saw the beautiful girl in bed, he raised his candle a little higher to make sure and said, "Oh Lord, the companionship was good, the prayers were good, the whisky was good but this is certainly the height of highland hospitality!"

In every little community in rural Cape Breton there was a dedicated body of women known as grannies or midwives. They were not graduates of any institution but learned their trade in the school of experience. In maternity cases they knew how to support the baby when it was being born, how to clear any mucus in the baby's air passage, and how to tie the cord. For most births they moved into the household and did the housework, as well as looking after the mother and baby. Sometimes they even helped with the barn work. For many years after medical services were available to rural Cape Breton, the doctor was called in only when there were complications. The midwife was called first, and it was she who decided whether it was necessary to call the doctor.

The first medical men to serve the Sydney area were the garrison doctors, Dr. Williams, Dr. White, and Dr. Inglis. Dr. White, a graduate of Edinburgh University, was a student of John Hunter, and a surgeon of marked ability. Dr. Inglis, a brother of Sir John Inglis, the hero of Lucknow, performed the first surgical operation in Cape Breton Island, about 1830. The surgery, performed on a man by the name of MacVicar of Clarks Road, was for a strangulated hernia. The patient was first drugged with laudanum and rum until he was almost insensible. Then he was stretched on a barn door with holes drilled in it and strapped down with ropes. The operation was successful.

Following the garrison doctors were the colliery doctors. The first name I found was that of Doctor Tom Jeans, who came on an immigrant ship and was employed in the Sydney Mines area. A license was granted to him in 1829 by virtue of the first medical act passed by the Province on May 29, 1828, "an act to exclude ignorant and unskilled persons from the practise of physic and surgery." The act didn't apply to any doctors appointed to any garrison or military camp within the limits of the province. The following year an amendment was passed so that it didn't apply to anyone who had been regularly employed in practice for seven years previously.

Dr. Jeans had an able assistant by the name of Dr. Duncan MacLarty, a brilliant graduate of Edinburgh in 1860. Dr. Louis Jacques practiced in Sydney Mines in 1855, became colliery doctor at Cow Bay in 1862, and retired from practice in 1870. Dr. Henry Kirkwood was colliery doctor for the Gowrie Colliery at Port Morien. He moved to Pictou in 1872 and afterwards sailed for Australia. Dr. Alexander MacGillivery, a native, began practice in Sydney in 1873 and died there in 1907.

The first hospital to open up in Cape Breton Island was the Marine Hospital in Sydney. There two mottoes hung on the wall of the convalescent ward, in full view of the patients. One read,

"All Men Must Die," and the other, "Prepare to Meet Your Maker."
The second hospital to open in Cape Breton was a colliery hospital,
St. Joseph's, in the Glace Bay area.

In Richmond County there was a Doctor Andrew Madden,
a native of Drumneath, Down, Ireland, a graduate of Dublin
University, who settled on Isle Madame. One story I found in
the Archives in Halifax is that he landed in the Strait of Canso
area in 1812 and wandered on horseback through various parts
of Cape Breton Island, applying his art whenever he had the opportunity. Other notes I found in the same file say that Doctor
Madden landed in the Strait area in 1817 and had a very active
practice for about forty years, by horseback, by foot, and by boat.
He died in 1858.

Dr. Henry Kline Fiscot, a Huguenot from the Isle of Jersey and
a graduate of Glasgow, M.R.C.S., in 1841, started a medical practice around 1842 in Arichat, serving a wide area of the county on
horseback. The brass plate on his door read, "Henry Kline Fiscot,
Accoucheur" (translation: a doctor who specializes in delivering
babies). Dr. Fiscot was joined by his brother, Dr. John Fiscot, in
1870. He died in 1887. Dr. Henry Kline Fiscot is credited with
being the first medical doctor on the Island of Cape Breton to
use the Smellie obstetrical forceps in maternity cases. (Note from
medical dictionary: William Smellie was an English obstetrician,
1697-1763, who devised several types of obstetrical forceps, some
with lock and curved blades called "Smellie's forceps.") Dr. Henry
James Fiscot, a son of Dr. John Fiscot, was a graduate of Harvard
University and practiced in Richmond County, but I could not
find any dates of that practice.

In 1876 a Dr. Robert who landed by the vessel "Maria" came
from St. Pierre et Miquelon and began practicing on Isle Madame.
He claimed to be a graduate of a medical college in Paris.

I have the names of many of the doctors who practiced in Inverness County between 1840 and the end of the century. The first regular practitioner to settle in Inverness County was a Doctor Noble who did his work on horseback and by foot. Dr. Henry I. Bisset, a graduate of Harvard in 1860, settled in Port Hawkesbury and died in 1887. In the book, *Cape Breton Ships and Men*, John P. Parker noted that Dr. Bisset owned sixteen shares of a brigantine built in 1860 by the name of *The Florence E. Matheson*. His investment came to grief when the boat was wrecked in 1867.

Dr. John MacIntosh, I believe, also practiced in Port Hawkesbury and was a graduate of Jefferson Medical School. He died in 1892. Dr. Hugh Cameron, a graduate of the University of Pennsylvania, 1861, settled in Mabou and died in 1918. Dr. Patrick Alex MacDonald, a graduate of Harvard in 1871, practiced in Port Hawkesbury and died in 1910. Dr. Angus MacLennan, a graduate of the University of Pennsylvania, 1872, was born May 3, 1844, at Broad Cove, Inverness County. After his graduation he settled in Margaree Harbour. He was M.L.A. for Inverness County from 1882 to 1886, and M.P. for Inverness County from 1896 to 1908. I have read that he was a fierce man in politics but in his medical practice he was as brave as a lion and as gentle as a lamb. He died August 27, 1908, in Port Hood, Inverness County. In 1872 a Dr. Robert Smith, a graduate of Harvard University, settled in Mabou. Dr. Duncan, another graduate of Harvard, practiced in Port Hood. He died in 1883. Dr. John Cameron, M.R.C.S., a graduate of Edinburgh in 1855, settled in Port Hood in 1883. He trained before the teachings of Dr. Joseph Lister and, although a surgeon himself, never accepted the principle of antiseptic surgery. Dr. Allen Kenneth MacLean, a graduate of Bellevue Medical School, practiced in West Bay and died in 1896.

Dr. Robert Gun, another graduate of Bellevue Medical School, graduated in 1874 and practiced in Strathlorne, dying in 1921. I was told a few years back by some of the older people in the Middle River area of Victoria County, that during the First World War years Dr. Gun used to drive through Galanders Mountain by horse and wagon in answer to their calls for help.

Dr. Lauchlin MacInnis was born in East Lake Ainslie. He graduated in medicine in 1858 and practiced in his home area for five years. His fee for medical services to subscribers was 12 shillings and 6 pence per person per year. He moved to Ontario and from there to British Columbia, where he became Mayor of the city of Victoria. A brother, Doctor Robert Thomas MacInnis, a graduate of medical school in 1869, settled in British Columbia. He became Mayor of the city of New Westminister 1876-1878, M.P. 1878-1881, the senate 1881-1887, and Lieut.-Governor for B.C. 1887-1900.

When I went to Baddeck in 1928, there was a Dr. Hugh N. MacDonald still living in Whycocomagh who was always referred to as Dr. Hoody. I feel I should include him among the pioneer doctors, as his heyday was in the latter part of the nineteenth century. He was employed by the C.N.R. when the railroad was being built through Cape Breton. Dr. Hoody graduated from Queen's University in 1882, and as well as being C.N.R. doctor, he did general practice, much of it down through part of Victoria County, and a large portion of Inverness County, as well. During his life, and after his death in 1939, his strength and physical prowess became a legend. In 1881, at the age of sixteen and still at college, he became a champion wrestler. While on a visit to the United States in his younger years, he apparently went to see a boxing match in one of the big cities. John L. Sullivan was the drawing card. After John L. had disposed of his opponent in the ring, he issued an invitation for anyone in the audience to come into the ring for a round. In less than a minute, Dr. Hoody was alone in the ring and John L. was over the ropes—so the story goes. Another story that has been handed down: Dr. Hoody was the only man ever known to buy a drink at a certain bar in New York, put ten dollars down, and get his change back.

There is a letter in the Archives in Halifax, in Dr. Hoody's own handwriting, in which he described a trip he had made in mid-winter from Whycocomagh to Ottawa Brook in Victoria County. The call came late in the afternoon, and it was dark and snowing when he got on the ice at Whycocomagh. Somewhere between there and the south side of the lake his horse went through the ice. He said it was no good to call out for help because the wind was blowing hard and the snow drifting and no one would hear him anyway. He unhitched the horse from the sleigh, pulled the horse out of the ice himself, put the horse back in the sleigh, and kept on his way. On getting to Ottawa Brook, he saw his patient and gave his horse a rest. By this time the storm had somewhat abated, and although the night was dark, he started back home. When he got back on Whycocomagh Bay, the storm grew worse. The doctor became completely lost and didn't know which way to head. Eventually he came to a shore. Not knowing where he was, he got the horse up in the woods and waited until morning. When day broke, the storm having subsided somewhat, he found he was on one of the islands in the Bay.

The first doctor in Victoria County was Dr. Joseph Elmsley, who was born Nov. 21, 1816, in Scotland, and graduated from Aberdeen University April 30, 1845. He began practicing in Baddeck about 1851. Apparently he didn't make too good a living, because in 1858 he accepted the job of Registrar of Deeds in Victoria County. Then in December 1859 he sailed for New Zealand.

Doctor S. G. A. MacKeen took up a practice in Baddeck in 1860. In the Archives in Halifax I found a note, written by Doctor George MacKeen, who said of his father:

> It is a pity my father did not have time to write a book on his experiences during those pioneer days in Victoria Co. I often heard him relate an account of a fierce trip he had in mid-winter from Baddeck to Bay St. Lawrence shortly after the Trans-Atlantic Cable had been laid and landed. One of the two operators in charge fell ill with diphtheria and there was no one within miles to nurse him or to relieve his partner. My father travelled by horse and sleigh, by snowshoe, and by dog sled over ice floes, and reaching the sick man, remained with him until he made a complete recovery.

Mrs. Alexander Graham Bell, many years after, wrote a four-act play entitled *Just an Incident*, in which she dramatized this trip north.

Doctor John Lemuel Bethune was born March 9, 1850, in Loch Lomond, Richmond County. He graduated from Dalhousie Medical School in 1875 and began practicing in Baddeck that same year. He was a community worker, a politician, a statesman, as well as being a medical doctor. J. P. Matheson, one of the old-timers in St. Ann's area, has a story about him:

"I remembered a time when there was a woman in labor on Rooster Hill, North River, and they could not locate Doctor Bethune. I was a very young man at the time. I walked up to Alex Governor's, Munroe's Point, who had the only telephone in the district. I found Dr. Bethune was down North Shore. On the way back I called at Morrisons' as I knew he had a good driving horse, a real good roadster. He said, 'You take my horse and wagon and go down there and get him.' I took the horse and wagon and started off.

"I got down as far as Indian Brook and called at MacDonalds,' who were running the Telegraph Office. I found Dr. Bethune was down at Wreck Cove, near Smoky. At MacDonalds' they told me to put my horse in and they would take their horse and go down to Wreck Cove and get the doctor. So I did. I put my horse in, gave him a feed and a rest, and waited. They came back to Indian Brook about ten o'clock that night. I landed the doctor up on Rooster Hill about midnight. Everything was all right in the morning. When I was driving the doctor back to Englishtown he said, 'I left my horse in Englishtown two days ago. I've been away two days and two nights. Do you know how much money I made on this trip?' I said I didn't know. 'Well,' he said, 'this MacLeod man gave me two dollars this morning. That is all the money I've seen since I left home.'"

J. P. said, "Those were pretty tough times."

Another pioneer, Dr. Dan MacDonald, came to Victoria County and started practice in Ingonish in 1892. In 1894 he moved to Baddeck, where he practiced until 1914, when he joined his army unit.

Dr. Roddie, a son of Dr. Dan MacDonald, recalled for me one trip his father made to Bay St. Lawrence by horse and wagon. The priest in Baddeck, a Father MacIntosh, was also called. Somehow or other, Father MacIntosh got hold of a tugboat and went down by water, arriving there much ahead of the doctor.

Dr. Roddie relates, "After my father made the 110-mile trip and treated the patient, the patient's husband fetched out from under the pillow a five-dollar bill and said to my father, 'Here's five dollars. Father MacIntosh wouldn't take it. Will you?' My father said no.

"Very often trips to Bay St. Lawrence, down and back, would take an entire week. He'd just get home when he'd find someone in the kitchen who had come in from Middle River for him. My father would say, 'If I'd known you were here, I wouldn't have come back.' But in the next instant he would say to me, 'Go out and hitch up the horse for me, Rod,' and away he would go again.'' Rod says his father always kept three horses.

In 1939 I had been practicing in Baddeck eleven years. I had had only one vacation, and that was in 1934. I was very tired and felt I just had to have a little time off. Dr. Dan MacDonald, who was then seventy-nine years old and had been retired for a few years, offered to relieve me for three weeks. He brought his violin along with him. The very sick patients he sent into North Sydney Hospital. For many of the others he played jigs and Scots reels on the violin. Everyone was happy when I came home. No one was sick.

When I started practicing in Baddeck in 1928, there was no hospital in the area. Maternity cases were all handled in the home. Roads were primitive by today's standards, and no one ever dreamed of plowed roads in the winter. There were very few days in the winter months that I didn't do at least fifty miles in the horse and sleigh. The record for time was one hundred miles between seven in the morning and eleven in the evening, with the same horse. Furthermore, that horse was in good shape after the trip. A week or more without sleep was common. The weather was unpredictable and, in winter and spring, often foul. I remember one trip in April in a rain storm that took twelve hours; when I got there I found it was a false alarm.

Yet despite the weather and road conditions, my years in Victoria County were happy ones. I feel my "Memoirs of a Cape Breton Doctor" is part of our heritage and should be preserved.

1

A BEGINNING

*I*t was five o'clock one afternoon in the middle of August, 1928, when I arrived at Baddeck, Cape Breton, in a new Essex coupe, to take up my practice in the village and surrounding area of Victoria County. Whether my arrival in Baddeck was the 17th or 18th of August, I can never remember. Whenever I wanted to find out for sure, I asked Kay Morrison: Kay was born about five minutes to twelve on the night of my first day in Baddeck—my first baby in the Baddeck area. There was no hospital in Baddeck when I first came here. Before we got one, I delivered more than two thousand babies in country homes, some more than a hundred miles from my office.

Normally the Baddeck medical practice covered an area 80 miles long by thirty miles wide, taking in all the area between Iona and Smoky Mountain, but there were years I had to answer calls as far north as Meat Cove and west much more than halfway to the Strait of Canso, a territory about 150 miles long.

It didn't take long for me to learn every highway and byway in the area I served. There were more night calls than day calls to homes located on the country roads. If I wasn't certain where the home was, I asked the family to "hang the lantern on the gate." For many years, "Hang the lantern on the gate and I'll be with you shortly," was my invariable reply to calls for medical help. In the winter and spring I often gave it with more confidence than I felt, because with snow drifts, ice, and sometimes mud, it might take me hours. Many times on bad ice I thought I would never see the shore again. But usually, on dark nights I could see the lantern on the gate, or its reflection, a mile or two away.

Many of my more memorable experiences were my struggles in all kinds of weather, over primitive roads, to reach people in need of medical attention. But not all of my travel adventures could be blamed on the roads or the weather. Shortly after I arrived in Baddeck, I was called to see Stewart, the eleven-year-old son of Johnny Sam and Carrie Campbell, the owners and operators of the Lakelyn Hotel. I suspected the boy had rheumatic fever. After watching him for a few weeks, I decided to ask for a consultation. I deduced that Stewart's rheumatic fever was complicated by endocarditis, an inflammation of the inner lining of the heart cavity. At that time, and up till just a few years ago, there were no medical specialists in Cape Breton, and I asked the family if I might call in for consultation Dr. Kennie MacKenzie of Halifax, who had been my professor in Medicine at Dalhousie. They agreed.

When I reached Dr. MacKenzie by telephone, he said he would depart that night by train, due to arrive in Orangedale at a time I had already figured out, four o'clock the next morning. I thought it proper I should meet him personally.

Early next morning, I left Baddeck by car, leaving enough time to meet the train even if I had a flat tire or something else went wrong. I arrived half an hour before the train was due. Swinging my car around, I backed into the station and got out. But I forgot to put the brakes on. Down a slight incline the car rolled, coming to rest with the hind wheels between the rails and the front end still on the platform. Then I heard the train's steam engine whistling and blowing.

In those days the trains could be heard from miles and miles away. But at that moment that train sounded very close indeed.

I rushed across the road to a home just opposite the station, got Murdock MacLean out of his bed, and told him what my trouble was. When he joined me on the station platform we could hear the train whistle blowing at every crossing. There were quite a few crossings in those days. Fortunately, we found some old railroad ties handy to the tracks. We used them to fill in the space between the hind wheels of the car and the platform. Then I jumped in the car, started the motor and drove her off the track onto the platform. This time I made *sure* the brakes were on. Quickly Murdock and I removed the ties from the track in order to avoid what could have been an even more serious accident. I don't believe we had two seconds between the time we got those ties off the track and ourselves out of the way and the train pulled in and lumbered to a stop.

When he examined the patient, Dr. MacKenzie confirmed my diagnosis. What we did by way of treatment, I do not remember, except that Stewart's condition improved. What stands out clearly in my mind was the near accident at the Orangedale railway station. That seems to me a good place to start my "How I got there, and how I got home" adventures.

Before I had been in Baddeck very long, many people would say to me, "Doctor, you should keep a diary, put all your experiences in it and then write a book."

I never kept a diary, first because I never had time to sit down and write notes, and also because I felt that what I was doing was probably no different from what was being done in many rural areas. But now I've come to realize that my experiences are a part of the folk history of Cape Breton, so I've tried to pull together, from my own memory and the memories of others, some experiences of the early years of my practice in Baddeck, as well as stories up until the time I was forced by my health to stop medical work.

My graduation in medicine was in May, 1928 from Dalhousie University, Halifax. Following this, I did a two-and-a-half month *locum* in Rose Bay, Lunenburg County. Although I was busy, I had a delightful time. The longest country call I made then was only seven or eight miles away, so I had plenty of time to enjoy the famous beaches of that county and an occasional picnic with the other young people of the district.

I had an agreement that when my locum was up at Rose Bay I would go to Bridgewater as an assistant to Dr. Rafuse. My father, however, kept writing me and telling me about the beautiful country in Victoria County. At that time he lived in Sydney and worked for the Excelsior Life Insurance Company, traveling all over Cape Breton Island.

In June 1928 I had to make a big decision. Dr. Dan MacAulay, Baddeck's beloved physician, had died. I drove to Bridgewater and discussed the situation with Dr. Rafuse, who released me from my agreement and wished me luck and happiness.

The decision I made to start my life's work in medical practice in Baddeck was not an easy one. But I never regretted it. In winter and spring my practice differed in no way from the days when the first pioneer doctors worked in the area. There were often times I had no rest for weeks. But they were happy years.

Renting a house from Ross MacAulay, the late doctor's brother, I opened my office on the first floor. I didn't live in the house myself, but boarded at the Hotel Baddeck for more than two years. I arranged with a family, in exchange for free rent, to occupy the house and look after my office. I got the best of that bargain. At that time the Hotel Baddeck was owned and operated by James Fraser and his first wife, Fannie. I paid eight dollars a week for room and board, and for this eight dollars I received the best of both.

In the wintertime my bedroom was off the hallway downstairs. The hotel telephone was just outside my bedroom door, convenient for night calls. When the tourist business started in the summer my bedroom was used as an office, and I had to share one of the cabins with Billy Mitchell, a boy still in his teens who started to work at the Royal Bank in Baddeck about the same time I arrived on the scene. While I used the cabin in the summertime, Mr. Fraser would have to get up at night to answer the telephone, then come wake me. Consequently some nights the three of us were disturbed three or four times.

Billy Mitchell and I had a grand time. He used to go with me on many country calls, especially on weekends, when he didn't work. Neither of us was a neat person. At first the young women who looked after the rooms tried to keep our cabin tidy, but finally gave it up as a hopeless task.

Having inherited most of Dr. MacAulay's patients, I was fairly busy from the start. Dr. Gillis, the other doctor practicing at that time in Baddeck, shared the burden, and for a couple of years the work see-sawed back and forth between us. If a patient didn't get along as well as the family thought he should, my work would slacken off and Dr. Gillis would become very busy. Then he would have the same experience. Unfortunately Dr. Gillis was not too strong physically, and about 1935 his health began to deteriorate. He died in 1937.

In the early years in practice, one of my greatest problems was to decide when my knowledge and ability were adequate for me to cope with a certain case by myself, when I should call in another doctor for consultation, or when to send the patient to a hospital some distance away. Surgical cases were, of course, sent to a hospital; to Sydney or North Sydney and sometimes Inverness for routine operations, or to Victoria General in Halifax for more complicated problems.

Another problem in the early years was learning to get along without so many of the diagnostic aids I had learned to use as normal procedure during my training. For instance, I was once called to Bucklaw, about twelve miles from Baddeck. Clarence Nicholson, a boy of nine, had fallen and injured his elbow. On examination, I suspected he had a fracture of the lower end of the humerus and a dislocation of the elbow. This, in my opinion, called for an x-ray examination, which meant a trip to North Sydney. When I told his father, he replied, "Gosh, Doctor, all the doctors who were here before you never bothered taking x-rays. I don't see why this boy should be x-rayed." So with this case and many others that followed, my diagnoses for the next several years had to be based upon clinical examination without the aid of any x-rays or lab work other than what I could do on the spot.

In Clarence's case I got out the chloroform bottle and proceeded to induce general anesthesia. In the country home, chloroform was the only general anesthetic we could use. We could never use ether because of the danger of spontaneous fire. Ether was a safer anesthetic, but it wasn't at all safe if there was a fire in the fireplace or in the stove.

I eventually got Clarence into a good sleep, at least as far as I dared to go with chloroform. The dislocation of the elbow went back easily; the fracture of the lower part of the humerus went into place when I flexed the arm at an acute angle with a little tension. I maintained this acute flexation by a slab of plaster and a collar and cuff sling. His father told me recently that Clarence, now past middle age, had no disability whatever from that accident.

I spoke recently with another early patient of mine, Francis MacNeil, who told me he was my first patient in the Iona area. Iona is thirty-five miles from Baddeck by road via the Little Narrows ferry, or twelve miles by boat. Although the mail boat went to Iona twice a day on schedule, sick calls were not on schedule. They came at any hour of the day or night.

"I was sick with pleurisy and pneumonia in the fall of 1928," Francis said. "You made seven trips to see me, Doctor. Some trips you made by boat, and some by car. The treatment then was different from what it would be today. I was drinking hot water then, and there were linseed poultices. The nurse was Katie MacLean, 'Katie Lighthouse' we called her. I must have been in bed two months, a long time, before I got over it right. They were pretty worried about me. I had great confidence in you. You got old Dr. Dan MacDonald up from North Sydney to consult, the two of you examined me, and then you went down to the front room of the house and had a talk. You both came up and told my Dad—I heard him saying afterwards—that you thought I'd come out of it all right. I did.

"After I recovered, you came to Iona many times by mail boat, and I drove you with the horse and sleigh or wagon when you couldn't get through with anything else. I drove you through Barra Glen, down to Gillis Point and caught the boat at Pine Brook or MacKay's Point on its return trip. You'd call at some houses there and the boat would wait for you. I've seen you going through roads, stuff that was something terrible, coming over here.

"A few years later," Francis continued, "oh, it must have been a good many years later, nearly twenty-five, you were over to my dad, Michael D. MacNeil. This was when you were the Member of the Legislative Assembly for Victoria, on the Liberal side. Dad was very sick. He had great faith in you, but this day he was pretty far gone. He was an awful Conservative. I remember him telling you, 'Look, Doctor, try and fix me up, so I can vote against you once more!' My dad did get better and lived to vote again."

Francis had another story: "Do you remember, Doctor, when you came over to my mother in the wintertime? The road was terribly slippery. Cars couldn't move at all—it was all one sheet of ice. You drove right along, didn't mind it at all. The road up to my mother's, we were working all morning trying to get it passable. We were trying to get our own car up the hill but could not. You came along, Doctor, and you never stopped until you got to the door. Someone asked you how you made it on all the ice. I remember so well your reply: 'What ice?' "

During my first year in Baddeck I got to know Dr. George MacKeen and his wife Queenie. He was retired then, but they were still living in Baddeck, so I made a courtesy call the first opportunity. I found Dr. George to be a fine old gentleman, but becoming a little forgetful. He wasn't practicing at all, but he was still able to do errands for his wife. She would give him a note of the errands she wanted done, something like this (I got this information from Mrs. MacKeen herself):

(1) Go to the White Store and get your groceries. Don't forget your cane.
(2) Go to the Post Office and get the mail. Don't forget your cane.
(3) Go to the Bank. Cash cheque. Don't forget your cane.
(4) Don't forget to come home.

That first day, as I was leaving the doctor and his wife asked me if I would give them what medical attention they needed for the rest of their lives. This I readily promised to do. Then they asked if, when they died, I would make a deep incision across the front of the forearm, thus exposing the radial artery. This was to make sure the doctor and his wife were not bleeding, that they were really and truly dead. After a few moments' reflection, I gave them a solemn promise I would carry out their wishes.

Dr. George died the following year at the Victoria General Hospital in Halifax. His body was brought home. When I went up to pay my respects, Queenie took me into the room where the body was and, closing the door behind her, reminded me of my promise. "He's been embalmed," I said, "and it isn't necessary." But she wasn't satisfied.

I had anticipated such an answer and I had brought along a scalpel, needle, and suture material, all done up neatly in a sterile package. Queenie stood alongside me while I made a deep incision and pointed out to her the severed radial artery with the embalming fluid oozing from it. She was quite satisfied. I did a neat suture job, pulled the sleeve down, and no one else in the village knew anything about it.

It was ten years later, in 1939, that Queenie died. I asked to be left alone with her body and very carefully carried out the same operation I had done on her husband. No one in the village knew it had been done.

Now, the story behind the MacKeens' unusual request had been explained to me the first time I called on them. It seems Dr. George's father had apparently "died" when he was nine years old and was put in his coffin. He remained there for two days. On the second day he sat up and crawled out of the coffin. Furthermore, he lived to put in fifty years of hard medical practice.

I used to call on Mrs. MacKeen occasionally after Mr. George died. On one occasion I was shocked to see her looking in such poor health. Trying to find out what was wrong with her, I started out by telling her how well she looked. Queenie said, "I'm feeling fine and I'm awfully glad to hear you say how well I look." I made some examination but couldn't come up with any diagnosis.

When I left the house Mrs. Walter Pinaud, who lived next door, came out to meet me. I remarked to Mrs. Pinaud how terrible I thought Mrs. MacKeen looked.

"I'm certainly glad you called," Mrs. Pinaud said. "I know for certain that that woman has not eaten one bite of food for nineteen days."

She told me she had promised not to tell anyone, but she couldn't keep the secret any longer.

"Well," I said to Mrs. Pinaud, "I'd better not go back to the house now or she'll know you told me. I'll drop in and see her again this evening."

I did, and after a very careful examination I came up with the diagnosis that she was dying from want of food. Queenie broke down then and told me she had only enough money left for her burial and this was the only way she knew to save that money.

In those days there was no such thing as Old Age Security. There was a Poor Committee in each district from which one could get a pittance. But Queenie was a very proud woman. She would rather starve to death than apply to the County Poor Committee. It was years afterwards that I found out from a young man who was working in the bank in Baddeck at that time that every month, as regular as the clock, a cheque had arrived for Mrs. MacKeen from the south. However, whatever fund her father had set up for her apparently stopped with the stock market crash in 1929.

I persuaded Queenie that whatever money she had left she'd better use as long as it lasted. I said, "You know if you died, someone would bury you anyway. You couldn't be left here." She laughed and agreed to start eating again. I figured if she had enough money for a good burial, it would keep her in food for a few months anyway.

Knowing Mrs. MacKeen very well, I knew I could not tell just anyone about her plight. However, I did confide her story to Miss Augusta McCurdy, who with her sister, Miss Caroline, lived during the summer months at Baycroft, their home at Baddeck Bay. A few weeks after this episode, I called again to see Mrs. MacKeen. Looking very fit, she told me that Miss Augusta McCurdy had come to her rescue and had settled one hundred dollars per month on her as long as she lived. Queenie lived happily afterwards, and I'm sure during those years no one ever knew the story, excepting Queenie, Miss Augusta, and myself. Now it can be told.

In December of my first winter in Baddeck I remember coming back from a call in Middle River. I was driving along in my Essex when a heavy snow squall came up. It was enough to make the snowbanks on Hunter's Mountain almost impassable by car. I suddenly realized that my car wasn't going to get me where I would need to go through the winter. On the spot I turned my car around, wheeled back, went to John A. MacDonald's in Middle River, and bought a mare—Gypsy Queen, formerly used by Dr. MacAulay. She came from racing stock and had lots of go to her, but she was a bit of a runt, no more than seven or eight hundred pounds in weight.

I wish I could recount now all the trips I made sitting behind Gypsy Queen during the three years I drove her. I remember paying forty dollars for her, but whether that included the harness or not I can't recall. I bought a sleigh from Ross MacAulay for twelve dollars that had belonged to Dr. MacAulay, too. Then I went to the White Store and bought myself a fur coat. The style in those days was to wear a 'coon coat in a horse and sleigh. 'Coon coats were quite expensive, a little too much for me, so I bought a "mountain goat" coat instead. It looked *almost* like a 'coon coat, much heavier, but no warmer. The coat cost seventy-five dollars and George MacRae, bless his soul, the owner of the White Store, gave me the whole winter to pay for it.

For twenty winters I sat in a sleigh behind a horse for most of my country trips. A strenuous life, yes, but not dull.

2

SNOW

During the first few months of my practice, I often had trouble finding the house to which I had been called. Sometimes heavy snow made it even more difficult. Once I was called to see Tom MacNeil at Highland Hill. Leaving Baddeck around eleven o'clock at night by horse and sleigh, I travelled through to Barra Glen. I had been told that to get to Highland Hill I should take the second road to my right, and that would bring me to where Tom MacNeil lived. I passed one road on the right. By this time, it was two o'clock in the morning. I came to a second road and took it, but I didn't notice that there hadn't been much traffic on it. I found the going very heavy for the mare, so heavy that at times she was up to her belly in the snow. At last, after a mile-and-a-half, the road came to a dead end. By this time the mare was floundering in deep snow. I realized that, instead of taking the correct turn, I had followed a wood road that someone was using to go back into the woods to cut firewood.

I had to unharness the mare, take her out of the sleigh, turn the sleigh by hand, then hitch up again, and go back down this mile-and-a-half to the main Barra Glen road. Finally, I found the right road and got up the hill to Tom MacNeil's.

It was between three and four o'clock in the morning when I arrived. Tom had a well-established lobar pneumonia in both lungs.

Now, this was *many* years before penicillin or any antibiotic, and pneumonia was the greatest cause of death. It had carried away most of our elderly people. I spent several hours with Tom, but my treatment was to no avail.

Another struggle against the snow was when I answered a call to a lumber camp in Upper Baddeck River. A man in the camp had been cut and the call was urgent. He was bleeding badly. A doctor was needed in a hurry.

A storm was just beginning to come up about the time I got the call. As I drove by the Masonic Hall, I noticed a number of people going in, so I judge it would have been between seven and eight o'clock in the evening. The trip would only be about twelve or thirteen miles.

The going wasn't too bad to Baddeck Forks because the snow was fairly level, but from the Forks on I had a tough time. I turned up the east side of the river before reaching what was then Everett Rice's farm. The first thing I met was a great big tree across the road. I thought first I would unharness Gypsy Queen and work her through the trees around the obstacle in the road. But the trees on both sides of the road grew so close together that you couldn't get a horse through, let alone a sleigh. I had no ax with me. I considered unharnessing the mare and then jumping her over the tree and finishing the trip on horseback. But this was impossible—I had two bags to carry and no saddle. I wouldn't be able to stay on as the mare plunged through snowbanks. So I had to find some other way of getting around that tree. I thought about going back to the Forks and up the other side of the river, but I knew the snowbanks along by MacPhee's would be so bad that a horse couldn't possibly get through.

I had learned by this time that in country practice one did not always have the instruments he needed. I had also learned that there was often some way to improvise that would solve the problem.

Then I hit on my plan. I was young and strong at the time. I broke the boughs off the tree by hand and brought Gypsy Queen up to the tree trunk. I picked up one front hoof and lifted it over the tree. I picked up the other and lifted that over. Then I got hold of one hind foot, lifted that up and over, and then the other hind foot. And there I was with the mare on one side of the tree and the sleigh on the other. I could have lifted the front end of the sleigh up, but I would have been in a bad position if the mare took a jump. I'd probably be jammed against the tree, in great danger of being hurt.

Meanwhile the storm was getting worse. In fact, it was difficult to breathe when I faced into the wind. The snow was several feet deep. I went behind the sleigh, burrowed a deep hole through the snow, down to the ground, and then burrowed a hole up underneath the sleigh until I could crawl under up to the front of the sleigh. Taking the sleigh on my shoulders, I raised it up enough so that I was half standing. I said, "Get up." The mare took one or two steps ahead and the sleigh was over the tree.

From there on, the going was very heavy and I was very uncomfortable. I was driving right into the wind, and breathing was difficult. We got stuck several times the next mile or so, but the mare worked her way out of the snowbanks. Then I came to the section called Upper Baddeck River Center. There was a bad spot there. Where the road crossed the river, there was a clean sweep of the wind across from the other side; a big snowbank blocked the road. Nearby was an old abandoned hall, once a church or a community hall. I got so thoroughly stuck in this snowbank that I couldn't move the mare at all. Working hard at this, I found myself short of breath, trying to pull the sleigh up out of the snow. I finally gave up, took my bags, and went behind that building for a rest.

I was standing there, half bent over, panting for breath, when something hit me in the back and hard enough to drive me headfirst into the snow. I couldn't imagine what it was. I lay there for a few minutes without daring to look around. I finally found the courage to turn around to see what hit me, and there was Gypsy Queen. When she had seen me go behind the building, she'd put an extra effort into getting out and followed me to shelter.

But in her struggle to get free of the snowbank, Gypsy Queen had overturned the sleigh. It was a good thing I'd taken my bags with me, because everything else that had been in the sleigh was buried in the snow. My buffalo robes, lantern, shovel and the rest of the gear weren't found until the following May, when the mail driver, John Dan MacKay, picked them up after the snow had begun to melt.

Less than a mile away from the camp, I noticed a light in John Dan MacKay's house. I was so cold I couldn't resist the temptation to stop. But barely had I reached the door when the mare took off up the road on the run. I ran after her and found her almost buried in the snow again. We overcame that obstacle and the mare and I arrived at the camp in a very few minutes, just about midnight.

I had to get warm first, and then scrubbed up. When I removed the bandage from the foot, I couldn't find the cut. "Oh well," I remarked, "it's a compensation case anyway." Then I pulled the skin apart and some bleeding started. It was just a small ax laceration that would have healed all right, I'm sure, without any stitches. But to justify my trip out there I thought I'd better close it with sutures, so I used local anesthesia and put in five or six stitches.

If it was hard for me to get through to a country call in the winter, it was often even more difficult to get a country patient from his home into a hospital.

The area between the Englishtown ferry and Smoky Mountain is always referred to as the North Shore, and several of my trips there were to see Donald Urquhart at Breton Cove, thirty-six miles from Baddeck. Donald had lobar pneumonia on one side of the chest, and in those days we usually looked for a crisis in nine days. Even before the ninth day Donald developed an erratic temperature and required constant attention. During the night he would get quite uncomfortable, and his family would panic and send for me.

Because of the hard driving conditions during winter, I could take Gypsy Queen all the way to Breton Cove. I would drive as far as Allen MacLean's in Englishtown, or Montgomery's in Jersey Cove and would leave her there. Someone met me there with a team, took me the rest of the way to Breton Cove, and then brought me back to my horse.

I remember well the last evening I went down to see Donald. I left Baddeck some time late in the evening when the temperature was twenty below zero. I got on the ice at South Gut and drove to Montgomery's in Jersey Cove. Just who met me that night, I can't remember. When I got to Urquhart's sometime after midnight, I put a needle in Donald's chest, as I suspected he might be developing empyema. Sure enough, I got a syringe full of pus. I tried to relieve the pressure, but he was still very uncomfortable, and we spent the rest of the night making plans to get him to the North Sydney Hospital.

Because of the weather, the only possible way to get him into North Sydney at that time was by horse and sleigh—the entire length of the trip from Breton Cove right to the hospital steps in North Sydney, a distance of over forty miles. We laid a mattress down in a wood sleigh, and put Donald on it, well covered with blankets. We left at seven o'clock in the morning, with the temperature seven degrees below zero. The date was March 14, 1929.

I recently asked John T. Urquhart, a cousin of Donald's, what he remembered of that trip. Here is his account:

"There were three teams. Dr. MacMillan and I were in Neil Urquhart's team; Donald's sister, Nan, was with John Alex Mac-Donald's team; Donald, the patient, went with Angus Urquhart in D. B. MacLeod's team. In crossing St. Ann's Harbour, we went on the ice at Jersey Cove near Montgomery's and came off at the Presbyterian Church in Englishtown. On Kelly's Mountain, we met the mail team. The mail driver tried to get his horse off the track, but the horse refused to budge. The snow was deep; it had been tracked down all winter. To try to get the mail horse to step aside was like asking him to jump overboard. We had to tramp down and shovel about seven or eight feet of snow, spending over an hour getting past the mail team.

"We went on the ice again below Malcolm Stewart's to cross Big Bras d'Or Lake, just east of the place where the Bras d'Or crossing is now. The ice at Big Bras d'Or was just drift ice that was stuck together. It took us from seven in the morning until six at night to get from Breton Cove to the Hamilton Hospital in North Sydney."

We never even stopped to feed the horses. We had intended to stop for a few minutes at Big Bras d'Or but Donald was so uncomfortable he coaxed us to keep going without a stop. I must have been worried about my patient, because John remembers that when we started across Bras d'Or Lake I told him I was afraid Donald would not make the hospital. He remembers my giving the patient a small dose of morphia by needle, which kept him fairly comfortable for the rest of the trip.

Shortly after our arrival, Donald was prepared for surgery and taken to the operating room. Dr. Dan MacDonald was the surgeon, Dr. Roy the anesthetist, and I assisted the surgeon. During surgery Donald went into shock, and for a while I feared for his life. His pulse went down until I could count only twelve beats a minute. Old Dr. MacDonald said, "Oh, he'll be all right; he'll be all right." I stayed with him for two or three hours after the operation until he began to recover and get stronger. I spent the rest of the night at Dr. MacDonald's home and got back to Baddeck, the next day although I cannot remember how; nor can anyone else.

As if this incident wasn't enough of a trial, Donald Urquhart gave me another good scare a few years later. Again, it was mid-winter when the call came, but this time it was an accident. Donald was working with a group of men at Jimmy Matheson's, sawing wood with a circular power saw. Donald was on top of the pile of wood when he tripped and went headfirst toward the saw. Fortunately, the operator saw him coming and turned off the power, but the saw was still spinning with terrific momentum. The power saw tore his scalp, and the whole top of his head was so gashed that I hardly knew where to begin or what to sew to what. He had bounced back and forth off the saw, each time hitting the saw and making another long gash from the back to the front of his head.

Before I got there, they had called Hannah Matheson, a trained nurse, who tried to control the bleeding until I arrived. I'm sure I was an hour and a half trying to get the bleeding stopped. I sweated gumdrops over that little incident. But the traveling was good that day; the entire trip took not much more than ten hours.

Another mid-winter trip my first year was to Humes Rear, in back of the Indian village of Nyanza, about ten miles from Baddeck. As usual, the call came in the evening. Billy Mitchell, my roommate, and I set out with Gypsy Queen and the sleigh. The snowdrifts were at least twelve feet deep, and it looked for awhile as if we weren't going to get through at all.

For over forty years I've puzzled over why that particular road was so bad that night. While making these notes, I talked to Duncan MacQuarrie, who was living at Humes Rear at the time. He told me that we had used the *summer* road. In the winter, that road drifted in badly, so the folks who lived around there had a certain track through the fields that they used instead of the road. No wonder we had such trouble!

But that wasn't the only "conspiracy of silence" we encountered that night. When we got to the house I found it was a case of terminal pneumonia. I did everything I could for the patient to make her breathing easier. We got every pillow we could find in the house and elevated her some. Her people gave us a room, and after we went upstairs, they brought us two pillows. Billy said, "I believe I heard them going into the sickroom downstairs and taking these two pillows from the patient." We didn't use the pillows at all. It wasn't long until daybreak, when we got up and had some breakfast. The patient was still alive, but the end was inevitable.

There were many trips in the winters between 1929 and 1931 when Billy Mitchell went along with me. On one call to Jack Churchill's at Upper Middle River, which was about fifteen miles, the day of snow and rain made the going extremely heavy. We struggled for some time with the mare and the sleigh until Billy complained of some heart palpitation and said he was quite short of breath. I just put it down to the extra exertion for someone who worked in a bank.

I've wished ever since that day that I had paid more attention to Billy's complaint. He made many trips with me during the three years he lived in Baddeck, and on one other occasion he made a similar complaint. But his association with me was probably a factor in his decision to study medicine. He resigned from the bank, returned to Stellarton to finish his high school education, and then went to McGill University to begin the study of medicine. For the first three years he received financial help from an uncle. Then, after the uncle's death, he took on a night job in the laboratory to finance his studies. His health broke under the strain. It was then that the doctors discovered that he had had rheumatic fever as a child which had damaged his heart valve. He was advised to drop his study of medicine.

He wrote me at the time that he was going to take the few dollars he had saved up and make a trip to California. Some time later he returned home on a stretcher. His family called me to say that he wasn't expected to live very long and that he wanted to see me. I couldn't get away right then, but planned to go to see him the following week. When I saw him, it was in his casket. If he had stayed on at the bank instead of becoming interested in medicine, he might have lived a few years longer.

One night in about 1930 I came home from the North Shore after two very busy days and nights. It was two in the morning and I was cold, colder than I have ever been in my life. My hands were so cold that I couldn't unharness the mare. I tried my best to get the traces off the whiffletree, but my hands were just too numb. I finally managed, with great difficulty, to get the belly girth unfastened. Then I got the hames unfastened and I slid the hames, the back pad, and the britchen backwards over the mare. I tried hard to get the collar unfastened, but I just couldn't do it. I finally turned the collar upside down and slid it over the mare's head. I got the bridle unfastened, which wasn't too hard, and then it was a matter of getting the rug on the horse. I got it on, but I couldn't fasten it. The next morning I got a good scolding from the man who took care of my horse because when he went in to feed her the rug was completely off.

Anyway, I went into the hotel and stood over the hot air furnace just outside the door of my room. I was still numb and shaking from the cold when the telephone rang. I won't say who it was, but it was only a drive of nine or ten miles out into the country. My caller was very worried: "My wife is *terribly* sick, and I'm very much afraid for her life. I want you to come out and see her right away, as fast as you can."

I realized I hadn't warmed up enough yet, and knew I would be unable to harness Gypsy Queen, but I knew it wouldn't go over too well if I told the man I was too cold to make the trip. So I answered, "Yes, I'll come, but you'll have to drive in and get me. My mare is completely tired out and she can't go another step." I knew he had a good horse that could make the trip in a hurry. "Well," he said, "when I come to think it over, perhaps she's not that bad. It may be just a bit of flu. How will it be if I call you the morning and let you know how she is, and then we'll see." Next morning about eight or nine he called me and said his wife was all right and it wouldn't be necessary for me to go out.

Mind you, this type of call didn't come very often. More often, I remember many times where a life was lost because I wasn't called soon enough. Perhaps there had been a belly-ache for a few days, but the appendix had ruptured before I received the call. There is no point in relating any of these stories, for they would only aggravate old sorrows.

Those winter trips were hard on Gypsy Queen, and once I thought I had lost her. Early in the morning of February 22, 1929, I was called to New Campbelltown to see Frank Dunlop. His home was just thirty miles from Baddeck via Big Harbour and Slios a Brochan (a Gaelic name: *slios*: a side hill near the water;

brochan—gruel). I made an early start, but when I got to the head of the Bay I found I had unbroken road. The snow wasn't very deep—about two feet—but there was a heavy crust that made each step a hard one. It took me until five o'clock to go the twenty miles to reach Frank, who was ill with lobar pneumonia.

After doing what I could for him, I turned right around and headed for home. I got as far as Charlie (Boxer) MacDonald's home in New Harris when Gypsy Queen went down. She was trotting, as much as she could in that kind of snow, or perhaps I should just call it a fast walk, when she went down as if shot. I thought my mare was dead. I sat there for a while with the reins in my hands and thought, "What the hell am I going to do now?" After a while she raised her head. I waited longer, and she got to her feet. I walked her to the MacDonald's house nearby and put her in the barn. I still remember what a good night's sleep I had that night. I guess Gypsy Queen and I were both worn out, because I was in bed before one o'clock and slept straight through until seven or eight in the morning.

About a month earlier, on January 5, I had a call to see young Kennie MacKenzie in New Harris. He, too, had pneumonia. It was a very cold night and I traveled by horse and sleigh. On the way down the mountain, some time near midnight, one of the chain traces broke loose from the hames and I began to worry about what would happen when I got to the foot of the mountain. I thought, "When this horse begins to pull, she's going to pull halfway out of the sleigh and dear knows what will happen."

Gypsy Queen was a horse who would never stop on the road unless you were strong enough to pull hard on the reins and set her right back on her haunches. If you wanted to stop her, you had to drive into a driveway or up to someone's house or barn. The only thing I could do was to jump out of the sleigh and run along with the horse down the mountain. I picked up the chain trace and fastened it back on the hames while she was still going. Then, when I tried to jump back into the sleigh, I missed the seat, made a dive, and caught the iron that ran from the box down to the rear end of the sleigh. I rolled over on my back and went down the mountain that way, on my back in the snow. Fortunately my big mountain goat coat protected me some. Near the bottom of the mountain, the sleigh began pitching and I got some bad bumps on the head. I had to let go, lest I get hurt. It was about a mile from Kennie Angus's house and I had to walk the rest of the way. Gypsy Queen went right on without me, turning in where she saw the lantern on the gate. She arrived at that call about an hour before I did.

Another mare that served me well was Tilly. She, too, had her own notions about how to behave, and that caused problems more than once. I remember a call to Iona one winter morning that meant driving across the ice to Washabuck and then over the mountain. The going was heavy, with just step-holes in places. As we were climbing that long hill at the head of Boulacet Harbor, I noticed that Tilly seemed to be having a hard time. I got out of the sleigh and walked behind to give her a rest. I hadn't been out of the sleigh for ten seconds when Tilly took off on the gallop up the hill. I knew if she ever got to the top I wouldn't see her for a couple of hours and I'd lose a lot of time, so I chased her up the hill and caught her just in time. But the exertion of running in the deep snow with my heavy coat on was too much for me. When I got back into the sleigh, I just collapsed. I couldn't even pick up the reins. Now we were going downhill, but Tilly resumed that labored walk, as though she wanted me to feel sorry for her and get out to walk again. But I didn't. Once was enough.

3

HELP FROM MY FRIENDS

*P*eople all over the country were wonderful about helping me get through to my calls. Sometimes I'd start out in a car and then find I needed to change to a horse and sleigh, and they were always made available to me, along with a bed or food or whatever else I needed. Often the men would go along with me if the driving was rough, to be sure that I made it safely.

Neil Morrison of South Haven made such a trip with me in late December 1930, when I was called to see Murdoch Campbell at Black Head, Englishtown. I made it as far as the Manse in my car and then hung up in a drift, so I went to Neil's home and explained my problem. He had a good horse and a good truck sleigh, which he loaded with hay in case I wanted to sleep. He drove me to Murdoch's, waited while I took care of the patient, and then we had a bite of lunch. On the way back we stopped to see Murdoch's sister, who was also very ill.

Neil recalled the trip home. "You lay down in the sleigh, stretched out, and went sound asleep and started to snore. I was afraid you were cold, so I covered you with the buffalo robe. You slept and you snored for seven miles. The road was heavy, so the horse could do nothing but walk along. Finally you woke up and sat with me on the seat. As we were coming to the Manse where you had left the car in a snowbank, we saw the lights of a car, piled up in that same snowbank. It was J. K. MacKenzie, who was driving Dr. Gillis down to a call on the North Shore. With all the territory you two doctors covered, you both landed in the same snow drift."

If snow made the going very heavy, sometimes a winter thaw made it even worse. On the evening of January 29, 1933, I was called to the home of Johnny MacRae's at the Plaster, about six miles from Baddeck. There had been snow earlier in the year and I had been using a horse and sleigh for some time. But then came a January thaw, so we were using cars again on some roads. You could get a car through at least the main roads by pushing hard, and I was able to reach the end of the Plaster road, where I was met by Johnny's brother, Roddie.

As soon as I saw the patient, I knew he had a ruptured appendix. The big question was how to get him to the hospital in North Sydney, a distance of thirty-five miles. We knew that, except for the snowbanks, we could push the car through the soft snow. But we also knew there were a lot of snowbanks between us and North Sydney. We decided, C. D. MacRae, Roddie, and myself, to put Johnny in the car and shovel and push our way through. We left the Plaster at ten and reached Ross Ferry five miles away between twelve and one o'clock.

Captain Carmichael had put the ferry up for the night in a protected cove and he told us it would be impossible for a boat to cross to Boulardarie that night. "My boat will be smashed and everyone will be lost," he told us. But I told him we had a man in the car with a ruptured appendix and there was no other God's way in the world to get him to the hospital but to get across the water on that ferry and then shovel our way to North Sydney.

So the captain agreed to try. He brought the boat into the wharf, but the water was so rough that first the deck would be way below the level of the wharf, and a few seconds later it would be several feet above wharf level. Roddie was driving the car, and he studied the timing of the waves for a few minutes before he made a try at it. He gauged the timing just right, and there we were on the ferry.

The crossing was very rough all the way, and getting off the boat on the other side was as bad as getting on. It seemed the boat was coming right down on top of the wharf. Finally we made it off, but just as we did, the engine conked out. We spent about an hour in a pouring rainstorm trying to dry out the distributor. After it started, we went along fairly well for about four miles, though the going was heavy. By this time, whenever we had to get out to shovel we were wading in snowbanks and slush up to our waists. There was a long snowbank at Big Bras d'Or through which we tried to push the car. We'd back up and then ram it ahead again and again. For a while we made progress, but then we seemed to come to an end of forward motion. I said to Roddie, "Let me try." I backed up about a half mile and got the car going. I hit that snow-bank and drove in, I suppose, a hundred yards. Then the shaft broke. So there we were—in a crippled car, in a pouring rainstorm, with a man with a ruptured appendix in the back seat.

There was nothing to do but get out. I stayed with the patient while the other men went looking for help. They woke up Dan Murdoch Patterson, who lived nearby, and he brought his horse and sleigh. We got the patient into the sleigh and the rest of us walked behind. By this time we had contacted Carl Alden, who met us with his car at the other end of the snowbank. We got in and started off, thinking there were no more snowbanks between there and North Sydney. We had fairly good going as far as Little Bras d'Or, but there we found Gannon Road into North Sydney completely blocked. We had to turn around and go through Sydney Mines. We arrived at the hospital about eleven o'clock in the morning after more than twelve hours on the road. Dr. L. R. Meech, the surgeon, was waiting with the O. R. all set up. I'm happy to say it wasn't too long before Johnny was home again and in good shape.

Jimmy MacKinnon reminded me recently of a trip I made to his home in Cain Mountain in the winter of 1933 to attend to his mother. "We were eating supper one night," he said. "It was hash we were having. All of a sudden, my mother swallowed a little sharp bone and it stuck down in her windpipe. I never saw any-one in such agony. You wouldn't think she was going to live five minutes, choking and trying to get her breath. One of the boys rushed off with the horse and sleigh to the nearest telephone a mile away to call the doctor."

When the call came in, I felt quite sure I could drive my car across the lake and up as far as MacIver's Point, only five miles from the MacKinnon home. There I would stop, flashing my head-lights on and off until they met me with a horse and sleigh to fin-ish the trip.

The plan almost didn't work. It wasn't snowing hard, but there was a terrific low drift on the ice, with the visibility almost nil. My lights were useless. I could hear the sleigh bells when they were to windward, and I would take off in that direction, but by the time I got there they were somewhere else. This went on for three-quarters of an hour before we met.

It was about twelve-thirty when I arrived at the MacKinnon home. Jimmie met me with the remark, "My God, am I glad to see you." Mrs. MacKinnon was in great distress trying to breathe. I could feel the piece of bone lodged in the opening of the windpipe and hoped I could get it with curved forceps. However, during my examination the bone became dislodged and in that second she swallowed and the bone went down her throat, lodging in the gullet under the breast bone. The real emergency was over. She could breathe again and everyone sighed with relief.

But when she tried to take a drink of water, it came back faster than it went down. When a foreign body sticks in the gullet, it produces a muscular spasm causing a complete obstruction. Someone served tea and a lunch while I tried to figure out my next move. I had nothing with me to serve as an esophageal bougie. "Jimmie," I said, "I'll have to go back to my office and get some instrument to push that piece of bone through to the stomach."

We decided that I would drive back to Baddeck in my car and then make the return trip by horse and sleigh. My big worry was whether I would ever be able to find my way back to Baddeck in the blizzard. When we reached my car we found the snow had banked all around it, and it took considerable shoveling before the car was free.

Luck was with me on the trip to Baddeck. I made the ten miles in not much more than ten minutes. Picking up a length of hard rubber tubing in the office, I hurried to the barn, hitched up the horse, and was on my way back to Cain's Mountain.

The tube I took back with me, which Jimmie called a hose, wouldn't work. I had to get out the chloroform bottle and give the patient anesthesia, and then try the tube again. This time it slid through to the stomach, taking the piece of bone with it. With chloroform anesthesia for a very short procedure, there is a quick recovery, and while we were having breakfast Mrs. MacKinnon was able to take some liquid food.

I was very happy, but tired. Jimmie reminds me now that I went to bed there and had three hours sleep before starting home. When

I arrived home, just before dark, there was a call waiting for me down the North Shore.

During Regatta Week at the Bras d'Or Yacht Club in 1967, I met a chap whose face I recognized but whose name I couldn't recall. He knew me, though, and we had quite a conversation before I finally admitted I just couldn't place him. "I'm Big Malcolm's son," he said. "Big Malcolm" was a retired R.C.M.P. officer we had here a number of years ago as a local policeman. His son told me that there was a story about me that had been going around for nearly thirty-five years and now that he was talking with me he wanted to find out whether it was true. I asked him what story *that* was.

"Well," he said, "the story goes like this. Away back in the thirties, you had several confinements due on the north shore about the same time in mid-winter. You figured the roads were pretty heavy and wondered how you were going to make the six different trips down there to look after all of them. So you made a special trip down by horse and sleigh. At every home where a baby was expected, you went in and gave special directions as to just how much castor oil to take, and just when to take it. You drove all the way through to Wreck Cove. Apparently your timing was very good, because you turned around at Wreck Cove and started back home and collected six babies along the way."

I'm afraid that story has become exaggerated over the years. Here's what really happened: During the late afternoon or early evening of March 20, 1935, I was called to deliver Mrs. Rachel MacAskill at Rear Little River, North Shore. It was a frosty night and I went by horse and sleigh, arriving late in the evening. At three the following morning the baby was born and was named Murdoch Angus

MacAskill. After we were through with our duties there, I went to Mrs. Hannah Matheson's home—she had been the nurse who helped me on the delivery. I'm told, although I don't remember it, that I received a call there asking me to go to Wreck Cove, and I set right off by horse and sleigh. I got back to Hannah's about five in the afternoon and decided I needed some sleep.

Before I went to bed, I asked Hannah to call Mrs. D. J. Smith at River Bennett and Mrs. Murdoch MacInnis at her husband's father's home in Breton Cove and instruct each of the women to take two ounces of castor oil. Then I fell sound asleep.

An hour or two later the telephone woke me. At first I thought it was morning, but it was still only early evening. Mrs. Smith was in labor. Although it's more than thirty-five years ago, I still remember the trip from Mrs. Matheson's home to the Smith's, a distance of about eleven miles. With every step the horse took, you could hear the shoes of the sleigh screeching with the frost. I reached Mrs. Smith in plenty of time and the baby was born at ten that night. That baby was Evelyn Smith.

Knowing that I had ordered Mrs. MacInnis in Breton Cove to take castor oil, too, I couldn't spend the rest of the night at the Smith home because there was no telephone. So I drove on to William MacLeod's two or three miles away, reaching there after midnight. They gave me the use of a bed, and I phoned the Mac-Innis family to tell them where to find me. William must have been in his late seventies then, but he got up and put my horse away for me. I went right to bed. But I hadn't been asleep very long when the telephone rang. I was so sleepy that I didn't really wake up, but started groping around my bedroom looking for the telephone. I went into every bedroom upstairs until I heard a voice say, "Doctor, the telephone is downstairs." Then I woke up completely and went down to answer it. Mrs. MacInnis was ready. Mr. MacLeod got up again and helped me harness up. I don't know what time I reached Breton Cove, but the baby, Anna MacInnis, was born at 4:00 AM on March 22.

Different people down in the North Shore area disagree on just what times the three babies were born, but it is a fact that two of them have their birthdays on March 21, and the third has hers on March 22.

I had another strenuous trip down to North Shore in 1935. I don't remember how far down the Shore I had been, but I do know I had been away from home two days and two nights and busy all the time. On my way home about midnight, as I was passing Port Davis with seven miles still to go, I saw a light coming through the field. Johnny Drover met me at the road with the news, "You're wanted back at Captain Kidd's at Black Head right away. It's an emergency."

"Captain Kidd" was what everyone called Dan Buchanan. He didn't approve of the nickname, as I found out when I wrote a prescription for him which the druggist mailed to "Captain Kidd," Englishtown. Much as he needed the medicine, he refused to accept it under that name. But he never succeeded in getting rid of the nickname.

When Johnny Drover told me I was needed there in a hurry, I didn't see how I could make it. I was very tired and so was my horse. Johnny didn't have a good horse at that time, so I had to figure out the closest place where I could get one.

I decided to go to "Red Dan" Smith's, about halfway between South Gut and Englishtown. When I arrived there about two in the morning, I got Red Dan out of bed. I told him I had to get to

Captain Kidd's and asked him if he would drive me. When I first woke him, and all the time he was dressing, Dan kept saying, "No, I'm not going. What do you want to go down there for? It isn't necessary at this hour of the night and I'm not going." I knew Red Dan pretty well and I knew he didn't mean a word of it.

Dan remembered it this way: "The doctor got to our place about two o'clock in the morning. Himself was very tired and his horse was tired, wet with sweat, and hungry. I had to turn out. We had no temperature gauge then, but I judge the temperature was about ten below zero, a February night. The roads were fairly good. The first thing I was up against, I had to take his horse out of the sleigh, put him in the barn, put a rug on him, and feed him and take care of him. Then I had to give a feed of oats to my own horse, get him ready, and get him in the sleigh. Indeed it was cold, a little breeze of northwest wind.

"We started off as soon as I had things readied. I was well acquainted with Captain Kidd and I was very eager to get the doctor to him when I heard he was sick. I had a good horse and we weren't very long going. The Doctor took care of him and then we started back. The first thing I knew, up around Whitfield's, Dr. MacMillan was alongside me snoring. You'd hear him a piece away. Before that he'd been talking to me and then suddenly he started snoring. I didn't wake him. He slept till we got back to my house, about half between daylight and dark in the morning. Dr. MacMillan got out and went into the house. I put the horse away and then went in. There was no sign of Dr. MacMillan. He'd found a bed and piled in. He slept till dinner time, with how tired he was. He left after dinner. Wherever he went, I don't know. He'd been through the mill."

On another mid-winter call to Englishtown, my own horse was tired from an earlier trip that day. I tried to pick up a horse from the livery stable, but they were all busy. I called Kennie MacRitchie of Baddeck Bay and asked him if he would take me by horse and sleigh to Englishtown if I got as far as his house. He said he would. How I got to Kennie's, I don't remember and neither does he. But he remembered the rest of the trip:

"It was March 14, 1938. The weather wasn't too bad when we started out, but as we got down towards South Gut, it turned very stormy. The wind was blowing from the nor'west, some snow, quite cold, and the temperature was crawling down around zero. From there to Englishtown, the horse could do nothing but just walk. We reached the patient, a Mrs. Fader, at Black Head about ten o'clock at night. I got warmed up while the doctor attended to the patient. We were there about half an hour and then the doctor said, 'Let's go back to John MacAskill's and stay for the night.' By this time there was a complete blizzard, and to think of getting a horse back home through the storm that night was just impossible.

"So, we went back to MacAskill's. I suppose it was near twelve o'clock when they asked us if we'd like to go to bed and we both agreed that we would. We went upstairs and I got into bed. The doctor was still walking around the room, trying to unwind, I guess, when Mrs. MacAskill called up that he was wanted on the telephone. Down he went. I heard him say, 'I'll be there. Hang the lantern on the gate.' He came back up and said, 'Kennie, get out of bed. We have to go to West Tarbot.' I said, 'No, it's too comfortable here. You take the horse and go yourself.'

"But the Doctor wouldn't let me get away with that. 'No,' he said, 'you have to come with me.' "

The way I remember it, when I was trying to get Kennie out of bed he asked me what was wrong. I told him that it was a maternity case in West Tarbot. And Kennie answered, "Oh no, tell her to wait until morning." Kennie remembers that we got on the ice at Englishtown schoolhouse and set out to follow the bushes.

I'd better stop right here in the story and explain about "bushing the ice." As soon as the ice was fit for a team, bushes were stuck in a hole in the ice every so many feet between land points, to serve as a guideline for travelers. "Bushing the ice" was a responsibility of county governments. Without these bushes as guides, it would have been impossible to cross the ice in these areas in stormy weather. Even at that, during a severe storm with poor visibility, it was all too easy to lose sight of the bushes and become lost. However, if you could keep the bushes in sight, they served their purpose remarkably well. Unfortunately, that night when Kennie and I were trying to get to West Tarbot was one of those times when the bushes didn't help much. Kennie continues the story:

"The ice was bushed but we couldn't see the bushes at all, it was snowing and blowing so hard. We had to make a circle in the drifting snow around the Englishtown entrance as it was always open water. We had to do this by guess, taking the direction of the wind and the time as our only guides to get into Jersey cove. We couldn't see a thing.

When we got into the Tarbotvale area, we stopped at Norman Carmichael's and woke him up to enquire whether the back road into West Tarbot was open. If it were, we could save ourselves two or three miles. We weren't that lucky, so we had to go all the way down to the other entrance, making our trip twice as long.

Kennie recalls: "We got into West Tarbot and it was really blowing, snowing, and drifting. It was three o'clock in the morning at least when we arrived at A. J. MacLeod's house. I think it was the horse that guided us the last half mile. We couldn't even see the horse, let alone what was in front of him. I put him into the barn while the doctor went in to the patient. When I went in, I saw a couch there near the stove, and I just laid down on it, coat and all, and went to sleep. When I woke up I heard a new baby crying upstairs, and the doctor came down with a big smile on his face and said he had added another boy to the family. About daylight, we had breakfast and started back home."

Apparently the weather had improved by then, because Kennie doesn't remember any travel problems on the way home. However, he does recall it as a long, slow trip: "We left for home at eight o'clock in the morning. Everyone in the area between Tarbot and South Gut knew the Doctor was on the road. How many calls we made that day I can't remember. I know we had two full-course meals and several lunches along the way. On some of the calls he was pulling teeth, and on others were people who were not feeling well and thought they'd better have the Doctor look in while they had the chance. I suppose these cases today would be called 'winter fatigue.' The next morning I heard by the grapevine that as soon as he arrived home he found a call to Iona waiting and took off across the ice."

By the winter of 1949-1950 roads had been improved and snowplows were used regularly. That winter I decided I could do without horses and depend entirely on the plowed highways to let ne get my car through. It was a good theory.

On Christmas Eve, Freddie MacCharles called me. He lived in the village then, and had just had a call from his old home out at MacCharles Crossing, about four miles from town. His mother was very ill, and from the information they gave him, it sounded like a stroke.

A storm was already brewing by the time Freddie called and snow was beginning to fall, the start of what turned out to be a very heavy snowstorm. Freddie recalled for me our strenuous trip out there that night.

"When I called the Doctor that evening, he said we should each drive out there in our own cars. I wondered why he wanted to take two cars, but I found out. I started out, and probably a half-mile from town I was following a sleigh track. I couldn't see anything in front of me. Suddenly I slid into the ditch. I got out of the car and about ten or fifteen feet in front of me was a horse and sleigh. It had gone off the road to allow me to pass, but I hadn't even seen it. I just followed its track, right into the ditch.

"About this time the doctor came along in his car, so I left mine in the ditch and rode along with him. We got as far as MacCharles Crossing, where my brother Andrew met us with a horse and sleigh and took us up to the house. Mother was quite sick at the time, but the Doctor attended to her and made her comfortable. After everything was over, Andrew produced a bottle of run. I made hot toddies and we all had a drink.

"Mother was resting well, so we started back home. We were driven back to the crossroads by horse and sleigh, and then we got into the doctor's car and started for Baddeck. But I didn't stay in the car long. Visibility was so poor and the road so bad, I had to walk in front of the car in order to keep it out of the ditch. By the time we were halfway home I was completely fatigued, and crawled back in the car. I remember the doctor telling me, 'That was good rum Andrew had. We should have stayed there.'"

That winter of 1949-1950, when I got rid of my horse, seemed to be just one storm after the other. Every time I was called out in the country it was storming. By this time we had a hospital in Baddeck (it had opened the previous November 11), and I tried to deliver all my confinement cases there, but it wasn't always possible to get them to the hospital. We had some fine weather about the first of the month and I had urged all my expectant mothers who were near term to go to the hospital while the driving was good.

But Mrs. Campbell had stayed in Jamesville, and now she was in labor. The road out to Jamesville, a distance of thirty-five miles, was in bad condition, heavy with snow, and it was still storming. Her husband had been afraid to start for Baddeck with her.

The public health nurse who usually accompanied me on home delivery cases wasn't available that night, but earlier I had met a nurse who planned to spend the night in Baddeck. I called her and asked if she would go on the case with me. She would be only too glad to go.

We got as far as the road in to the Little Narrows ferry, eighteen miles from Baddeck, but we couldn't get any further. We walked from there to the ferry—over a mile in deep snow—carrying our bags. It was midnight or after by the time we crossed on the ferry.

Alex MacLennan met us there and took us in his horse and sleigh. When we got to Cain's Mountain, we met Hughie Murphy of MacKinnon's Harbour driving his jeep. He was a snowplow operator in this area and was on his way to work. Hughie takes up the story:

"I took the doctor and nurse in the jeep but only got a few miles as the traveling was heavy and we got hung up in a snowbank. The snowplow was in that vicinity but was out of gas. While we were wondering what to do, Jim Rory MacNeil came along with a horse and sleigh. He took Dr. MacMillan and the nurse to the Campbell home. We shoveled out the jeep, but it was waterlogged and wouldn't start, so we left it alongside the road and walked to Campbells.' When we got there we found that the doctor had decided the patient must go to the hospital."

By that time in my practice I had handled more than two thousand deliveries in the home, and I was well equipped to handle an ordinary case there. But here was a breech presentation with extended legs, which sometimes makes for a very difficult labor. There would be a considerable advantage, especially for the baby, if I had the patient in the hospital.

"You told me to go up to John R. Campbell's and borrow his car," Hughie remembers. "And you said if he refused me the car, take it anyway. I walked up to Campbell's store, and it was one of the hardest decisions a man ever made in his life. Mr. Campbell told me he would lend me the car on condition that my brother Peter drive it. We went back to the house, picked up the patient, the doctor, and the nurse, and started off. Meanwhile, the doctor had called from the telephone next door and ordered the Baddeck plow to meet us at the ferry. The last thing Mr. Campbell said when we were leaving was, '*Do not* let Dr. MacMillan get behind the wheel of that car!'

"When we arrived at Little Narrows there was a long snowbank. A couple of people were out shoveling. Dr. MacMillan got in behind the wheel and just drove the car through. When we got to the ferry, ice was jammed in between the boat and the dock. Long planks had to be used to bridge the ten-foot gap. Dr. MacMillan drove on there, the same as if he was on a paved highway. The road was plowed on the Northside Little Narrows, and we didn't stop until we came to the end of Buckwheat Road, where the road was completely blocked. There was over eight feet of snow in Johnny Sandy's snowbank and three cars completely buried. You could see the antennae sticking out of the snow. I had met the doctor at five-thirty in the morning and by this time it was around eight in the evening. I hadn't eaten all day and was completely starved. The doctor went into the MacRae residence to call a snowplow and while he was on the phone we helped ourselves to a cup of tea. The doctor had to do some fast talking on the telephone, because the foreman at the highway garage was afraid of putting the big plow (the only one available at the time) across the Nyanza Bridge. However, the doctor won, as he usually did, and we were mobile again in short order.

"The baby, Michael Alexander, was born about twenty minutes after we arrived at the hospital. When I got back home, about midnight, Mr. Campbell came out with a lantern and walked all around the car, inspecting it. He told me he had never expected to see his car back again in such good condition."

THE "SNOWMOBILE"

*I*n the fall of 1931 I began answering calls by snowmobile. Now by the mid-1960s snowmobiles had become a commonplace around Baddeck. They're now used primarily for recreation, although a few farmers and workmen back from the roads use them in their daily work. But my snowmobile was a *different* machine altogether. Even today, when I mention it my wife remarks, "That monster!"

And a monster it was. It consisted of all sorts of extra parts added to my own car to provide traction in the snow: there were skis mounted in front under the radiator, six wheels in the back, three on each side, and great big tractor belts around them. The rear tires had special lugs that fitted into the little openings in the belts. The contraption was geared so that when the speedometer registered seventy m.p.h. I was only travelling about twenty-five.

The doors of the car were cut in half, with only the upper part opening. I had to crawl over the tractor belt to get in or out of the car, and this was always a worry to me on bad ice. If the snowmobile broke through the ice on the lake and I had to leave it in a hurry with the tractor belt still in motion, the chance of survival would be no better than that of the proverbial snowball you know where.

When I first had the snowmobile made, I hoped it would solve a lot of my winter problems. And for a while I had a great time with it. When the snow was packed, I could go over the tops of fences, across the ditches and through the fields. The first time I used it was on a call to see Mary Bell MacRae in Gold Brook on December 23, 1931. I don't remember any problem with it, so I guess it went all right. But more than once the rear part broke through the ice. The skis in front kept that part of the machine up while the tractor belts ground away at the edge of the ice and the snowmobile inched ahead on an uphill climb until we were on solid ice and the thing leveled off. It was always a terrible feeling for a few minutes.

Once on Nyanza Bay, Gordon MacIver was with me and we really broke through the ice. When we had finally pulled out and were on good ice I stopped and we walked back to look at the bad spot. There was twenty feet of open water. There had apparently been an open crack in the ice that filled in with snow and then formed an icy crust on top. The weight of the snowmobile was considerable: the weight of the car, plus the extra wheels, and 200 pounds for each of the tractor belts, plus Gordon and myself.

Such incidents bothered me, but I still thought it was a good machine for country calls when the roads were snowed in. Toward spring of the first year I used it, I realized it wasn't the answer. I started for Big Baddeck just after a fall of very light snow. Just over the top of the hill, while still within the village limits, a great bank of snow with a face on it seven or eight feet high had formed across the road. I drove right into it, expecting the snowmobile would ride the bank. Instead, the vehicle just buried itself until I could hardly get out the window. I left it there and walked back to the livery stable where I hired a rig and driver for the trip.

On another trip, this one to West Middle River, it was after dark when I started out. Just outside the door, I met Harry Fraser and I asked if he would like to come along. My machine was a novelty in those days, and most people wanted to have a ride. Harry was no exception, and we took off. That short drive lasted three days and nights.

Harry remembers the trip: "It was a Wednesday and pretty stormy when we left Baddeck. We got as far as Frank MacGregor's in Nyanza, where we ran into a snowbank and buried the machine. We couldn't get it out so we left it there and walked back to Jack MacRae's.

"We borrowed a rig from Jack. He loaned us a mare that was in foal. The snow was all the way up to the mare's belly, but we took very good care, giving the mare her time.

"It was stormy and hard to see where we were going. It was past midnight when we reached the patient's house in West Middle River. We went inside and you attended to the old lady you'd been called to see. By this time the storm was raging outside and it was impossible to even think about starting back before daylight.

You sat in a chair and put your feet up on the heater and slept all night that way. I slept on a couch in the kitchen.

"Before I went to sleep I noticed a big dish of oatmeal porridge cooking on the stove and I remember thinking, 'Well now, we're going to have a good feed in the morning.' We did have a good breakfast in the morning, but that big bowl of oatmeal stayed on the kitchen stove. We didn't have any of it at all. I always wondered who they were saving it for."

Harry and I left about daybreak the next morning. It was still snowing and blowing and the roads were closed. There were no snowplows at that time so we had to break the roads ourselves. We returned the rig to Jack MacRae in Nyanza and decided to try to get the snowmobile out of the bank. Sometimes that would take a lot of time and a lot of shoveling, and this was one of those times. Finally we got it free and I decided to go out on the ice for the trip home.

Harry picks up the story: "I was kind of leery about the ice. Up to this time there had been no cars on the ice that winter and there was probably two feet of snow. We went out on Nyanza Bay, and followed the bushline to what we called Long Point and then headed away from the bushline towards Baddeck. It was not long before we were lost.

"You stopped the car and I got out and stood there for a few minutes and looked down at the ice. I could see the water coming through it. I said, 'Boy, you'd better pull this machine out of here. She's going to go down; the water's coming through fast.' You made a circle and I crawled back into the machine.

"It was blowing and drifting hard, but the snowmobile made such deep tracks it would take them a while to fill in. Our only hope was to get back to Nyanza before these tracks were covered.

"You said to me, 'Watch the bushes now and I'll drive,' so I stuck my head out the window. It was very blustery out there. You couldn't see a thing through the windshield. When we got back to Nyanza, my eyelids were frozen together.

"We came ashore near the wharf, drove down the road, and buried the machine again in *exactly* the same spot as the night before. We walked back to Jack MacRae's and stayed there another two nights and a day, waiting for the weather to clear. By Friday night, of course, they were hollering for the Doctor in Baddeck, but the weather was such that neither man nor beast could get through.

"Saturday morning was a little better and a group of men from the Baddeck Shore area, Herbert Anderson, Lauchie MacDonald, Johnny Roberts, and quite a few of them, came out to open the road. They all had heavy horses, the lead horse just pulling a log. They got the banks clear enough so we could get through and we reached Baddeck on Saturday afternoon about two. We were pretty cold, I'm telling you, and I was glad to get back."

And then, I remember a call that involved my snowmobile, a good walk in heavy snow, two horse-and-sleigh rigs, and an airplane. I believe this was the first time a plane figured in my practice.

On the evening of February 22, 1932, I was called to see Dave Proctor in Middle River Center. He had severe pain in his stomach and was unable to move. It had been storming for several days, dumping three or four feet of snow on the roads. There was an advantage in the old party-line telephone system: Everyone on the line listened in, and we had a conference about how I could best get through to see Dave. The road over Hunter's Mountain was banked with snow and impassable, and on the shore road to Nyanza there was at least one snowbank that would be impossible to get through.

I told the folks on the line that I might be able to get to Nyanza with the snowmobile, using the ice on the lake. The plan was to have someone meet me there with a horse and sleigh. By the time I started out, the storm had abated and vision was clear, but the going was heavy. It took me an hour to do the nine miles to Nyanza.

But there was no team there waiting for me and it was very cold; I tried to keep warm by setting off through the snow carrying two heavy bags. After covering about a mile and a half I was met by Johnny Bentick MacRae of Lower Middle River. Johnny Bentick told me that Dave's uncle, Duncan Nicholson, had started to meet me but by the time he reached Johnny's place the horse was worn out and Duncan was near frozen himself. He had put his horse in and asked Johnny to meet me.

It was twenty-nine below zero that night in Middle River. The rest of the trip was uneventful except that when we arrived in Middle River Centre one of my bags was missing. The box sled we were using had overturned several times, so I sent Duncan back to look for the bag while I examined the patient. It was fortunate that he found the bag and returned, because that bag was the one with my supply of morphine. The diagnosis was gangrenous appendix.

It seems I must have diagnosed this case before I left home, because all the way out I was trying to figure how in the world I was going to get him out of Middle River and to the hospital in Sydney. The roads were such that it would be impossible to get by horse and sleigh to the railway station at Iona to catch the morning train. There was only one possible way to get him out. I gave him a good heavy shot of morphine, then called the Cape Breton Flying Club and made arrangements for a light plane to land in a nearby field as early in the morning as they could.

Dave remembered this trip later: "I was taken from my home about two or three miles on a truck sleigh drawn by a horse. I was there about half an hour before the plane landed. They took me out and put me in the plane and we started off. There was no cover over my head and only a windshield to protect me from the draft. The plane was open underneath. The pilot said, 'Whenever you feel anything moving under your feet, let your feet slide with whatever moves.' I did as he said, and we landed in twenty or twenty-five minutes on the ice in Sydney Harbour."

He was safely in the hospital and had had his operation long before I got home. Roy Nicholson, another uncle of Dave's, drove me back to my snowmobile in Nyanza, but with the cold weather we'd had that night, the engine wouldn't turn over. I spent most of the day getting it started. I had to get someone with a blowtorch to crawl in under and put the torch to the oil pan. The oil was almost frozen. It was night before I got the engine warmed up, and late night before I got home, many hours after Dave's surgery had been completed.

Now, I've already talked about my mountain goat coat, but the demise of that coat is a story in itself. I was faced a decision involving the compromise of one or the other of my prize possessions. I had been making a call at Johnny Bentick's, and when I came out of the house I found the radiator of the snowmobile was frozen. In those days we only used alcohol for anti-freeze, and it evaporated rapidly. It had not been frozen long, so I took off my coat, put it over the radiator, and started the engine. Leaving the engine running, I went back in the house for a while. The radiator thawed out fine, but my fur coat was baked to a crisp. That was the end of my mountain goat.

On March 3, 1932, I was in West Middle River with my "monster." While there I got an urgent call to MacInnis' Cove for a delivery case I had been expecting. The patient was a Mrs. Cullins who was staying with her brother, Neilie MacInnis.

After finishing my work in West Middle River, I set out, driving down the west side of the river. I planned to put the snowmobile on the ice at Nyanza and drive across to MacInnis' Cove. But just by the store in Nyanza, the snowmobile threw a track. By that time I was a pretty good snowmobile mechanic; I always carried nuts and bolts and little wrenches, and usually when she threw a track I could put it back together myself. But not this time. Part of a track was bent and I couldn't repair it. As I stood there debating where to go for help to get me to MacInnis' Cove, A. D. MacRae of Middle River came along in a horse and sleigh. I grabbed my bags, jumped in his sleigh, and told him I had to get over to the South Cove area right away.

We crossed Nyanza Bay, passed Long Point, trying to keep out of the deepest snowbanks and the deep ponds. Ponds on the ice were always a danger in late winter. A few days of thaw would melt some of the ice and then a few cold nights would freeze over the top, so you couldn't see that there was water underneath. You knew there was solid ice down below somewhere, but you never knew how far down it was.

The short way to the MacInnis home was down the ice, parallel to the shore. But near the other shore we found so many ponds of water, and the ponds so deep, that we decided to leave the ice and try to make it through the woods. I picked a spot where I thought the road was near the shore, but I was wrong. I chose the worst spot in the whole country to leave the ice and go through the woods. The road was nearly a mile from the shore and we had to cross a salt-water pond.

On the way across that pond we got into so much slush and so much water that we were both standing up on the seat of the sleigh while the horse was very nearly up to his neck. It looked for a while as though we might lose the horse, but he made his way across the pond and some considerable distance through the woods in deep snow before we came to an open field and eventually to the road.

I was in plenty of time. Mrs. Cullins was herself a trained nurse and was not unduly anxious about the delivery, though she *had* been concerned about how I would get across the ice. That was the night Peggy Cullins was born.

I took Ralph Pinaud with me on a snowmobile call to Gold Brook, Middle River. People had told me that I couldn't make it up the Gold Brook road, even with the snowmobile. The snow was far too deep. I was instructed to go up what we now call the old Margaree road on the other side of the river as far as the Mac-Charles school house and cross the river on the foot bridge. Someone would meet me there with horse and sleigh.

Ralph was good company on the trip. He always had a line of stories that helped pass the time while driving, although the trip was uneventful. I attended to the patient and then we were driven back to the foot bridge where I had left the snowmobile.

Ralph remembers the trip home: "It was one o'clock in the morning when we arrived back at the snowmobile. The doctor said, 'Let's set a record; let's drive through to Lakes 'O Law.' In those years this part of the country at the height of winter was no man's land. There was no track on the road. It was impossible to tell where the road was. Sometimes we were in the ditch and several times over the edge of the bank. When we got to the second lake, what did the doctor do but head right out on the ice. I didn't know whether to swear at him or say my prayers. However, we had a grand time for an hour. We made so many tracks on the ice that when we started for the shore we were lost and it took a while to find the track where we got on.

"It was five o'clock in the morning before we were back in Baddeck. The doctor stopped the snowmobile at Bethune's Garage to let me out to walk home. I'll be damned, when he went to start it, didn't a track fly off right there. We both had to walk home."

The last trip I made with the snowmobile was in 1934. I was going down to the North Shore, and invited Urban Noel to go along for the drive. We took the ice at South Gut, planning to go ashore at Jersey Cove. But just opposite Murray Mountain we ran into a few deep snowbanks and broke a shaft. This wasn't the first time that had happened. I had had the snowmobile in the garage so often that winter and I was so disgusted with it by this time that I got out and walked away, and that was the last time I ever drove it.

My homemade snowmobile may have been thirty years ahead of its time, but it was a temperamental old machine. It only got six miles to the gallon of gas, and it broke down at the most inopportune times and in the most inconvenient places. It spent a lot of time in the garage and it cost me more money than I ever made on the calls when I used it.

And it was dangerous. I had many narrow escapes with the snowmobile, especially when traveling in stormy weather on ice. If I told them all, many people wouldn't believe them. And those who did believe them might lose their confidence in me as a man of good judgment.

5

DEDICATED HELP

*T*he great event of my life, the one that brought me the strength, comfort, and courage one must have in the medical profession was on October 4, 1930, when Miss Ethelean Parker of King's County became, as she remains, my wife. She unfailingly provided the warm home life I needed. She brought up our son and daughter, often in my absence, and was able to carry on her own shoulders the problems of the home without putting more worry than was necessary upon me. Her worries must have been formidable when I was out for days and nights in succession, in impossible weather, and unable even to get messages through. But there were two *other* people who became part of my life in the late 1930s who were of great help to me and to the community at large.

First, in 1937 I hired Jimmie MacIver (Little Jimmie) to look after my horses and barn. Then the Public Health Department of Nova Scotia sent a Public Health Nurse, Miss Phyllis Lyttle, to Baddeck to give health service to Victoria County.

Jimmie started to work for me in the fall of 1937. That first winter he was with me I still did all my own driving, but when the next winter came, Jimmie took over. He was my constant companion on the road for eleven winters and had complete charge of the horses. He was on call at all hours, as I was, and if he worked twenty-four hours a day, as he often did, that was all right with him. If we got into trouble Jimmie did the worrying. I just did what I was told.

No matter how short the call at a country home, the horse was always unhitched from the sleigh or wagon, rubbed down, stabled, and fed if necessary. The well-being of the horse meant as much to him as the health of the patient did to me. It was a big help to me not to have to worry about both. A well-cared for horse can give terrific service in return. That I had.

When I visited Jimmie while gathering these stories, he was happy to reminisce. I asked him to recall some of the trips we had together and to compare the life of a doctor in the '30s and '40s with that of today.

"A doctor has a good life today," he began. "One thing, though, I had a good life with you because we got a lot of tea to drink. Every place we went, we had a drink of tea. But a doctor didn't have an easy life at that time."

Then he began to recall specific trips. "Do you remember the night we went down to Norman MacAskill's? It was snowing and blowing a gale, the wind right in our faces all the way down. The temperature was below zero and between the ferry and the other end of the beach going down it was terribly cold. When we got to MacAskill's house about one in the morning, you were so cold you had to stand by the kitchen stove for half an hour before you could examine the patient."

Jimmie remembered that the trip back was easier because the wind was then at our back and the cold not as penetrating. We left at four in the morning and stopped at Dan Montgomery's in Jersey Cove to call the ferryman. We waited in the warm house fifteen or twenty minutes to give the ferryman time to get out of bed, get dressed, and go down to the ferry. Then we made a call at

Dan MacAulay's on the mountain road at Englishtown where we had a good breakfast. Jimmie gave the horse some oats while I took care of the patient, and then we were on the way home.

Sometimes when calls piled up, Jimmie and I would start out in opposite directions. Jimmie recalled one such time: "Do you remember the time you got the call to see David Morrison in Tarbotvale and at the same time a call to Nyanza? The word was that you could reach Nyanza by car, but going north to Tarbotvale you could only get as far as South Gut. So you took the car and headed for Nyanza and I took the horse and sleigh and drove out to South Gut. There was a bank of snow just at the Presbyterian Church that I knew you couldn't get through, so I waited there for you. I'm sure it wasn't more than five minutes before you arrived. It was just past midnight then."

I stopped Jimmie at this point in his story, because I remembered that story better than he did. It was the night the horse, Jack, tipped us out and ran away. That was the only time I saw Jimmie let go of the reins. But I can't really hold that against him. When the horse tipped us out, the sleigh tipped on Jimmie's side, and when he hit the ground, I landed on top of him. I can still hear the wind going out of his chest. He completely lost his breath and he couldn't help letting go the reins.

After Jack tipped us out, he headed toward Rockyside. We had planned to get on the ice at the wharf at South Gut, but Jack saw a track leading toward Angus MacDonald's, and he followed it. We were sure that the horse would turn in at Angus's because the road from there to Englishtown hadn't been opened all winter, so we chased after him. It was two miles and up hill all the way. We were sure he wouldn't try to go any further, especially since he was still dragging the sleigh on its side. It had stayed tipped, and one shaft was over the horse's back and the other between his legs.

At Angus MacDonald's we found the horse hadn't stopped there, but had kept plunging through the deep snow, and we knew we couldn't catch him. So we turned and walked back down the hill to Murdoch Rob MacLeod's where there was a telephone. By this time we had walked four miles. We woke Murdoch Rob and he telephoned ahead to Angus Morrison in Englishtown.

Angus said, on the other end, "I think I hear the bells coming now." He dropped the receiver, jumped into his clothes, and got down to the road in time to catch the horse. He put Jack in the barn, fed him, and let him rest until we arrived. Murdoch Rob drove us to Englishtown on the ice, and after breakfast there we harnessed Jack up and started off again. By this time the horse was rested and seemed none the worse for his wild trip. The sleigh was scraped on one side, but otherwise undamaged. We arrived in Tarbotvale about eleven hours after leaving Baddeck, and it was late that evening when we returned, after making several other calls around North River.

Another story that stood out in Jimmie's mind was the time we had to roll the horse out of the snowbank to find some footing. We were going down to Christie Effie's at North River Bridge, about twenty-three miles from home. "Gee, talk about storming!" Jimmie said.

We didn't have too much trouble getting as far as South Gut, but from there it was bad. Murdoch Dan, who was driving the mail to Tarbot, had put up there for the night. He had sent word through that it would be impossible for him to get home that night. We learned that Christie Effie had phoned South Gut to find out whether we had passed there yet, and Maggie MacQueen, the telephone operator, had told Christie, "A dog couldn't get through the roads tonight."

When we told Murdoch we were going through anyway, he decided he had best go, too. It wouldn't do for the mail to be delayed if the doctor could get through. We waited while he hitched up, and then I got in the sleigh with Murdoch for a change and sent Jimmie on ahead. The road through North Gut was heavy and slow; it was blowing hard. We kept the conversation up, though there were times we could scarcely hear each other.

The snowplows had made a big cut in the bank at Munroe's Point, but the snow was drifting so badly that it had filled in. The going was almost impossible. In the sleigh ahead Jimmie was having trouble. He was actually crossways on the road, trying to drive the horse up the face of a drift, but he didn't know it. He didn't know why the horse wouldn't go ahead. Murdoch Dan and I got out of our sleigh and walked up to help him. Once he got the horse pointed up the road instead of up the snowbank, he was all right.

The next trouble spot we had was down at the little turn by Dannie Kennie's, where we got stuck in a snowbank. We still had two miles to go. Our horse strained so hard to get through the drift that he broke his harness, not once, but three times. Each time we took the horse out of the sleigh so Jimmie could patch the harness. Jimmie always carried an auger, leather straps, brads, and a hammer with him, and he could patch up any harness that broke on a trip. But we still couldn't get through the snowbank. Finally, the horse was down in the snow. We unhitched the sleigh, pulled it back from the horse, and then the three of us rolled the horse over three times, across the ditch and up into the field where the snow wasn't so deep and where the horse could get his feet on solid ground. About half a mile after this, we found the road level and open and had perfect going right down to Christie Effie's, where we stayed the rest of the night.

Jimmie remembered another time when our horse had performed valiantly. "We went down to Wreck Cove all the way with our own horse, a distance of forty-five miles. On our way back we had a call from Little River and had to turn around and go back there. We headed for home a second time and were stopped by someone who told us we were needed back at Little River again. When we finally reached home about eleven o'clock that night, we figured we had done one hundred miles that day, all behind the same horse."

In 1938, the year after Jimmie started working for me, Miss Phyllis Lyttle came to Baddeck as Public Health Nurse. After that there were often three of us in the sleigh. Neither Jimmie nor Miss Lyttle ever complained about the hours or the work load.

Miss Lyttle did complain to me however (years later) about the reception I gave her when she arrived in Baddeck. She had stopped in Sydney on her way back to Baddeck and someone there had told her, "You'll love to work with Dr. MacMillan; he's a wonderful man to be associated with in any kind of work." Miss Lyttle was a brand-new nurse, fresh out of McGill University, and she was escorted to her new post by Miss Martell who had previously done tuberculin work in several counties of Cape Breton.

Recently Miss Lyttle remembered our meeting: "When I was taken into Dr. MacMillan's office, the first thing he said to me was, 'Where are you going? What are you doing? How old are you?' His questions floored me. How could anyone love to work with a man who would ask questions like that of a brand-new nurse sent to help him? I didn't like it a bit."

As sometimes happened, my wife soothed the situation. She asked Miss Lyttle where she was going to live and offered to let her share a room with one of our children until she found a place. Miss Lyttle later found out the reason for my brusque questions: "I'm sure my first reception would have been entirely different had Dr. MacMillan been told that a nurse was to be posted to Baddeck. No one had advised him of this fact and *naturally* he wondered what was going on.

"I found work difficult at first because the roads weren't paved and I wasn't used to driving a car. But I soon found that if I was going to work in Baddeck I would have to set up terms of reference with someone and know where I was going and what I was going to do. The doctor and I developed a way of working together that was not always agreeable to the Public Health Department, but it seemed to work for us. It was a source of real pleasure, once I got started. My ten and a half years there certainly made a public health nurse out of me.

"It didn't matter to the doctor what I would suggest, or where I wanted to have a clinic, or what time I wanted to have it. As long as I could arrange a clinic at a time when he could get there, everything was satisfactory. Sometimes he got some money from the people, and sometimes he didn't. That was no problem to him.

"There were times that we would leave the office at six o'clock in the morning by horse and sleigh, travel across the ice to Washabuck and then on to Iona and have an immunization clinic there at nine o'clock in the morning. I doubt you would find a doctor today who would say yes if you approached him with the proposition, 'let's have a Clinic in Iona tomorrow. Of course, the roads are closed and we'll have to leave at six by horse and sleigh to make it in time.' "

Arranging for inoculation clinics was a major part of Miss Lyttle's responsibility. We usually inoculated the children in the spring and fall of the year. In order to get one hundred per cent of the children in the county done, it was necessary to go into every district. The work was done in the local schoolhouse, and the nurse organized it all beforehand. It's fortunate she was a good organizer, because we ran a very tight schedule. The preschool children of the district would be brought into the school at the stated time. When we arrived, all the children would be lined up and the teacher would already have listed names and ages. We could do forty or more children and be out of the school and on our way in a very short time. Because of my practice, I could only go out for clinics every other day, and of course there were times when I had to leave a clinic and come home for some emergency. But three times a year, we visited fifty schools between Iona and Capstick.

Miss Lyttle recalled that she had a problem securing her immunization supplies: "I had one syringe, two needles, and one gauze bunch. It didn't matter how large the clinic was, that was all I was sent. It didn't take Dr. MacMillan long to find out that he might as well give me the supplies, because I couldn't seem to get them any other way. So, he provided the supplies and we got the job done."

Once we had the preventative work well in hand, I asked Miss Lyttle if she would help me on confinement cases in the homes. She was anxious to do it because she had never attended a home delivery. Before she left Baddeck in 1948 she and I had attended over a thousand confinement cases in the home, although such duty was not called for as part of her service in the Department of Public Health.

I remember one confinement case, about thirty miles out in the country. It was a primipara and a slow case, so we spent the night there. I managed to get some sleep during the night while the nurse stayed on duty and called me at times when she felt it necessary. In the morning, around ten o'clock, Miss Lyttle disappeared for a while and just after she disappeared, the woman went into heavy labor. However, she was back in time to get scrubbed up and gowned, so everything seemed all right.

Just as we finished taking care of the patient, we were called on another confinement in the same area. While the nurse was in the bedroom preparing the patient, I heard the two of them laughing. I tried to find out what the joke was, but they wouldn't tell me. After that delivery we had about twenty miles to drive by horse and sleigh, and again I asked the nurse what had been so funny. She finally relented and told me the story.

It seems that when she had disappeared on the first case, she had decided that she really had to go to the toilet. She went outside and followed the path over towards the woods where the outhouse stood behind some trees. After some distance of punching through the knee-deep crusty snow, she stopped. It was a Sunday morning and she was out of view of the house. She didn't have to worry about traffic on the highway because there were no cars on the road at that time of the year. If there happened to be a sleigh coming, she knew she would hear the sleigh bells. So she said to herself, "Gosh, I'm not going any further. This is just as good as going to an outside toilet." So she took a couple of steps into the woods, and tramped down a place in the snow. Just then, she happened to see two barrel staves there and she thought, "That's a great place to put my feet." The instant she got both her feet on the barrel staves, they began to move and she found herself weaving around the trees, over the brow of the hill and down. She lost the skis but kept going all the way down to the foot of the hill. She suffered a few painful scratches and bruises caused by the crust, but she must really have scrambled back up that hill to get back in time for the delivery.

Miss Lyttle was a good sport about all the difficulties that came her way on country calls with me. Jimmie MacIver remembered a time when the three of us set out to answer a call at Neilie MacInnis's at South Cove. Miss Lyttle and I drove in my car as far as Inlet, while Jimmie drove there in horse and wagon. He was going to borrow a sleigh from Dan Hutchinson to drive us across the ice. But when we got there, Jimmie remembers, "We couldn't get the horse on the ice because the ice near shore was so bad. Doc and Miss Lyttle started walking. They hadn't gone very far before Miss Lyttle went through the ice into the water up to her armpits. The doctor tried to make her go home with me, but she wouldn't do it. She took off her rubber boots, poured the water out, put them back on again and kept walking."

The three of us had many hair-raising adventures together. I remember the night of February 28, 1948, when Jimmie, Miss Lyttle, and I were going north on another confinement case. We got on the ice at South Gut and it was so foggy we didn't know for a long time where we were. We had to travel very carefully, as we were afraid of driving into the mouth of Englishtown Bay and right into the open water. Once or twice we crossed some cracks and we had an idea those cracks crossed to Munroe's Point. This gave us a clue which way to head.

"Every once in a while," Jimmie recalled, "the Doctor would turn to Miss Lyttle and say 'Can you swim, Lyttle?' She was awful scared, you know."

We finally picked up land around the Murray Mountain and just kept off shore enough so we wouldn't be in the brooks, and followed down until we came to the head of Jersey Cove. It was six o'clock in the morning when we reached Malcolm Dauphinee's home. We went right in and asked Mrs. Dauphinee how she was feeling. She said, "I'm feeling fine." I asked if she'd had labor very long. "Oh no," she said, "I haven't had any labor pain yet, but I have an idea I might be going into labor soon and I thought I'd better call you down." It was apparent there was no need for us to stay with her right then, so Miss Lyttle and I walked down to

Donnie MacDonald's and had breakfast there and a little sleep. Jimmie took the horse back to Arthur Buchanan's and put him in the barn there for the day.

During the morning Miss Lyttle and I walked up to the Dauphinee house again, and Mrs. Dauphinee was still feeling all right. We walked back to MacDonald's and had dinner. When we returned to Dauphinee's in the afternoon, there was still no evidence of labor. So back to MacDonald's we walked. We were having our supper when I looked out the window and saw a horse coming on the gallop with someone standing in the sled. I jumped up quickly because I knew they were coming for us. Mrs. Dauphinee had gone into labor all right, and in a hurry. We had only a quarter of a mile to go and it took only a very few minutes, but by the time the nurse and I got to the house, the baby had been born. The baby weighed 13 1/2 pounds and was a girl. They named her Elizabeth, and she is herself a trained nurse now.

So there it was. We had been lost on the ice all night, spent all day waiting there on the North Shore, and the baby got there ahead of us after all. We did what needed doing for the mother and baby and left for home. It was almost morning when we reached Baddeck.

Miss Lyttle may not have enjoyed all of our winter experiences on the ice, but she enjoyed still less being left behind. She remembered one time when that happened: "Sometimes in bad weather the doctor would decide he preferred the driver of the sleigh, Jimmie MacIver, to the nurse. One Saturday night I gave up something I particularly wanted to do, went with the doctor to South Gut in the car, and then transferred to the sleigh with the doctor and Jimmie. The horse went through the ice a couple of times near the shore, and we all had to get out to help him, each time getting wetter and madder. Then finally the doctor told me to go home; the sleigh was just too heavy with the three of us in it. I went home all right. I took the doctor's car and I had no intention of going back to South Gut in the morning to pick him up. He could get home any way he liked. But his wife sort of made me feel that that wasn't what I should do. I should go down and pick him up, so of course all was forgiven and forgotten in short time."

Jimmie remembered another time he and I took off for Gillis Point in a snow storm, leaving the nurse at home because the storm was too heavy to risk three in the sleigh. On the way across the lake, we lost the bushes. One of them had blown out in the storm, and because the snow made the visibility virtually zero, we couldn't find the next bush. After a while we found another sleigh track, then another, all joining. We realized we had been going in a circle and following our own track all the time. We stopped the horse and I began circling around on foot, calling back and forth to Jimmie so he would know where I was. Finally I found a bush and I stayed there until Jimmie caught up with me.

Being lost on the ice at night in the middle of a storm is always a frightening experience. It happened to me more often than I like to recall. Another such time was when I answered a call to Christmas Island, which is near Grand Narrows on the South Side of the Bras d'Or Lake. The man who phoned said that if I could get the car across the lake to Shenacadie, the road was good from there to Christmas Island.

I was a little nervous about the ice that night and took Jimmie with me for moral support, even though I was driving the car rather than going by sleigh. One always feels braver when he has company.

The visibility was very poor on the lake due to a low fog, but we knew the ice was bushed all the way across. The usual crack from MacKay's Point to Boulardarie Head was open wide that night and we couldn't find any place we could cross it. Following the crack to the shore at MacKay's Point, we were able to get around the end of the crack on the shore over the ice cakes. From there, everything should have been clear driving. But in trying to pick up the bushes again, we wandered too far from the south side of the crack. We were completely lost. It was not a very good feeling.

With the best of ice conditions there were some parts of the lake one always avoided. First we tried driving in circles, hoping to find the bushes. No success. So we attempted to head out in a straight line. We knew there was open water to the west near Iona, open water to the east, Big Harbor way, and to the north toward Baddeck there was a crack in the ice open about seven feet. We had one chance in four of making a landfall. Surprisingly, we came ashore quicker than we expected, only to find we were back in Baddeck again. Some way or other we had come back across that crack, but we don't know where or how. It will always be a mystery. It was good to have a known starting point again, and this time we were a little more careful, staying close to the south side of the crack after getting around it on MacKay's Point until we found the bushes and we made it to Christmas Island in about an hour.

There were other repercussions from the nurse that I had to face— for instance, when she heard I had been over to Frank MacNeil's, Gillis Point, and delivered twins without taking her along. The call came about four o'clock on a Sunday afternoon, March 9, 1941, at the height of a snow storm and blizzard. I had visions of being lost on the ice while crossing the lake or stuck in a snowbank going over the Washabuck Mountain. By this time I had great faith in Jimmie. I knew for that kind of weather, three in a sleigh would be too many. It was dark by the time we got on the ice of Bras d'Or Lake, but occasionally between the gusts of wind and snow we could get an outline of the hills of Washabuck. Going over the Washabuck Mountain we upset a few times, but the most of the snowbanks our horse (Jerry Bars) waddled through.

Years later when talking to Frank about this trip, he said when he first put this call in to me I was at Baddeck Forks on a confinement case and the message was relayed to me. Frank repeated several times that the storm was so bad and road conditions so poor that they never expected to see me in Gillis Point that night, even though they knew I had started. Mrs. MacNeil remarked, "When Doctor MacMillan came in that night, before the twins were born, I was standing by the kitchen stove. He said to me, 'What the hell are you doing here?' and sent me to bed. It was not long after that the babies were born."

When I brought the first baby out, I gave it to Frank to hold. (This was a custom of mine. No matter how many people there were in the home the baby was given to the father to hold.) I said, "Frank, here's the first one but there is going to be another." He laughed, thinking it was a joke. In about fifteen minutes, I brought out the second baby. Frank came up half way out of the chair, half standing with the first baby on one arm. He said, "Jesus Christ! It is twins!" Their names were Carleton and Michael. After I got back from that trip, Miss Lyttle didn't speak to me for two or three days.

The hazards of travel were not the only dangers Miss Lyttle faced. I well remember a confinement case in mid-winter in the Gillis Point area that caused me great concern at the time. The wind was out of the northwest, and it was very cold. We had a stove with a fire going, right in the room where the patient would deliver, but in spite of this there was a draft coming in around the windows and other places. We had time on our hands and we spent it plugging up all the places where the drafts were getting in. I think before we were through you might say we had the place hermetically sealed.

About the time the patient was near delivery, we closed the bedroom door and the nurse began to arrange things. She took a bottle of chloroform out of the bag. Usually I carried my chloroform in small bottles, just enough for a case or two, but on this occasion I had a pint bottle. Somehow or other, she dropped the bottle. When the bottle hit the floor, it broke up completely, letting out the entire sixteen ounces of chloroform. Not one ounce of this chloroform went on the floor. It immediately diffused through the air in the room. The patient went to sleep immediately, and so did the nurse, but she managed to stay on her feet somehow. For some reason the chloroform didn't bother me at all. Miss Lyttle then started to cough. She was standing there, sound asleep and coughing. I opened the door to get us a little more air and finished the delivery without further incident. It was a year before Miss Lyttle recovered from that cough. She tells me now there are still times, particularly when she has a cold, that she has the same cough back and that it lasts about a month or more.

I'm afraid Miss Lyttle sometimes got the worst of it on our country calls. "You could always put one over on me," she recalls. "Regardless of whether there was a bed or not, you always managed to get a little sleep. If there wasn't a bed readily available, you would talk the expectant mother into getting up and taking a little walk. 'It'll be better for you, you would say.' And then as soon as she was out of the bed, you were in it. That was probably good for the mother and the doctor, but it wasn't very good for the nurse. It wouldn't matter whether there were little things or big things or whatnots going all around the room, it never bothered you. You would sleep on. Sometimes it was a little difficult for me, but if the nurse was going to go, she had to follow along and keep the same hours as the doctor, but without the benefit of those little naps. Still I doubt there's a doctor today who would keep the hours you did."

I'm sure she was right in scolding me a little about this, because I remember an instance in 1941 when the nurse assisted me in three maternity cases, one after the other, without any chance for rest, although I got some sleep on each of the cases. These three cases kept us busy from some time during the day of June 19 until six o'clock in the morning of June 21.

I can't remember who the first case was, but the second one was at Alfred Campbell's on Hunter's Mountain, and the third one was at George Bartlett's in Baddeck, the morning Sharon was born. All three were primiparas. They were all persistent occipit posteriors, which gave the doctor as well as the patient a hard time. During each case I thought, "Now this case would have done a lot better if I had sent her for a Caesarean," but after they were through, both mother and baby were perfectly well, and there were no complications.

We finished the third case about six in the morning and came back to my house for coffee. Miss Lyttle was extremely tired, so tired that I knew she wouldn't be able to sleep when she went back to her boarding home. I gave her a grain and a half of Seconal a few minutes before she left my house. When she got to her boarding home, she found she couldn't walk up the driveway; she had to crawl. Somehow she got in the house and reached her bedroom upstairs. The next morning Mrs. Philip MacLeod, her landlady, saw the nurse's door closed, assumed she was out somewhere on a case, and didn't open the door. When Miss Lyttle didn't show up by four in the afternoon, Mrs. MacLeod opened her door. There she was, lying across the bed with all her clothes on, still sound asleep.

In April 1940 the doctor practicing down in North Victoria telephoned to say he thought he had a case of diphtheria at White Point. He had no diphtheria antitoxin and wanted to know if I could get some down. It was spring, but back in those days the roads were often worse in spring than in the middle of the winter. Miss Lyttle and I started out with a good supply of diphtheria antitoxin. When we got over Smoky, we picked up the Health Nurse down North, Miss Nellie Wylde. We reached Neil's Harbour by car, but could go no farther, as the main road (Cabot Trail) was blocked with snow from Neil's Harbour down.

If you look at the map of Victoria County, you'll see where White Point is located and why getting there was a problem. There was no road at all between Neil's Harbour and White Point at that time, except a kind of path through the woods. We picked up Frank Dowling with his horse and sulky at Neil's Harbour and started through the woods. Mostly we followed a brook and had to wade through it because the sulky could only carry our bags. We had to walk the four miles and arrived at our destination about two in the morning.

The patient, Russel Dunphy, had a very nasty looking throat. I took swabs and gave him very large doses of diphtheria antitoxin; I also gave the other members of his family prophylactic doses of the antitoxin. The lab reports showed later that he had not had diphtheria but some sort of fungus infection of his throat. I found out later that some of his family had had heavy reactions to the antitoxin, but when you are practicing medicine that far away from a laboratory facility, you just have to go ahead on the assumption that the diagnosis is correct. This was a case where it was much better to be safe than to be sorry.

Neil S. MacLean of Washabuck recalled a time when Miss Lyttle and I had an unusually hard time getting home from a confinement case. We had been called over to attend Mrs. Michael Joseph MacLean. Apparently it was in early winter, because it was snowing hard but the lake hadn't frozen yet. The lake was so rough in the afternoon that we had to get the mail boat to take us across to Washabuck. By midnight when we finished the case the storm had become much worse, so bad that the ferry wouldn't come back to pick us up.

Neil takes up the story: "My brother, John D., was in Baddeck at tha' time. He had a fairly large motor boat, so we got in touch with him. He said he would try to come over, but wasn't sure whether he'd make it or not. We went down to the wharf and John D. was just at the shore before we could see him at all. It was snowing, there were gale winds, and everything was white. The sea was running so high that John D. couldn't tie the boat to the wharf. The doctor and Miss Lyttle jumped and they both landed safely on the boat. They'd only left the wharf and weren't out twenty feet when we lost sight of them, due to the snow and blowing. They finally arrived in Baddeck, though I didn't think myself the boat would ever, ever reach Baddeck."

The boat had a little cabin the nurse and I could get down in. Every once in a while, the boat would do some extra rocking and I'd wonder if John D. was still on deck. I'd poke my head out and say, "Are you there, John D.?" He'd say, "Yes, I'm still here, hanging on." But I still don't see how he hung on without getting tossed out of the boat that night, or how he navigated in such poor visibility. However, he was a man who spent a great part of his life in these smaller boats.

We came around the eastern end of Kidston's Island and were only a few feet from shore before we could see the flash of the lighthouse. When we were tying up at the Baddeck wharf, I asked John D. if he had a compass. He said, "No." I was glad I hadn't asked him earlier.

Another faithful and dedicated helper during those early years was Jessie Ann MacLeod. She managed to give me considerable assistance in my office in addition to her duties in the house. My wife and Jessie, between them, kept in touch with me all the time, no matter where in the county I might be, so that they could reach me in case of emergencies.

Besides performing her household duties, Jessie sterilized instruments, developed x-rays, and helped in many other ways. In those early years, before the Public Health Department got a mobile x-ray machine, we used to hold chest clinics in my office each spring and fall. All the known chest cases and known contacts were x-rayed, and it wasn't unusual to have forty people at a clinic. It was our custom to invite anyone in the waiting room at noon to come into the kitchen for dinner. Jessie remembered one day when we had more than fifteen patients at the table. "We had to have three sittings and we served them baked halibut. That evening your wife had two tables of bridge. You played for a while, but then were called away. I was a little suspicious that night that you didn't want to play and when someone called you to ask a question, you decided you had better go out to see them. I remember spending that evening in the dark room developing the x-ray plates. I loved doing that work."

Jessie also remembered the time that Mrs. Allan Austin MacNeil came across the ice from Iona with a badly cut hand. She had cut her fingers with a hatchet while chopping fish. Just before she arrived, I had left for a confinement case in Middle River. Jessie waited for a while until she thought I might be through with the delivery, then started trying to reach me by telephone. But something had gone wrong with the telephone line to Middle River and no calls could get in there, though calls could be made out. About nine o'clock that evening I phoned in and Jessie told me of the patient waiting. I told Jessie to keep her there, that I would be home by midnight, despite the storm, which was still bad.

Jessie had a long wait with the patient. "She stayed on and I stayed up with her. We didn't touch her hand. She had it all wrapped up, so we just waited. That was a very long night. It was nine-thirty in the morning before you got back. I talked with her all night and then gave her breakfast before you arrived."

There is another story I must tell about the time when Jessie was with us. One day, I was working with some fuming nitric acid in the office After I finished with it, I was returning it to the basement store room, when it dropped out of my hands. I had taken the top off before I brought it upstairs, and when it dropped, the entire contents came out through the neck of the bottle and splattered me from head to foot.

The first thing I thought of was a young medical student, who had put a small bottle of nitric acid in his hip pocket to take home. He planned to do some experimental work. It was in the winter, and on the way home he slipped on some ice, fell, and broke the bottle. He had to walk home before he could change his clothes, and he was burned so badly that he died. That story flashed through my mind.

So I dashed up into the kitchen and stripped right down. My wife and Jessie were there, but it was no time to be modest. I just got all the clothes off and started washing myself. My wife and Jessie thought I had taken leave of my senses. They didn't know what was wrong until my wife picked up my trousers from the floor and gave them a shake. All she had left was the belt. The trousers disappeared entirely into ashes, along with the rest of my clothes.

Jessie recalled a day in mid-summer of 1938 when I was called to Washabuck. The motor ferry came over from Washabuck to pick me up, and Jessie saw us leave the harbor. Minutes after that Kinnon Morrison was brought to my office, badly burned and almost out of his mind with pain.

Jessie went right to the telephone and called the wharf. "For gracious sake, if you can find a boat anywhere, go find Dr. MacMillan. He's on his way to Washabuck in the Washabuck ferry. Catch him and get him back here as fast as you can." Then she called Mrs. Sadie Currie, a trained nurse, to come over to see what she could do to relieve Kinnon Morrison's pain until I arrived.

I remember that we were almost to the Washabuck shore when I happened to look back and saw MacManus's big power boat coming in our direction. There were two men standing in the bow of the boat, waving to us to stop. I knew right away they were looking for me. Something must have happened in Baddeck, an accident of some sort. The boat was still a long way from us when I turned to the ferryman and said, "Look, there's something wrong. There's been someone badly burned in Baddeck." Why I said that, I don't know. Those words came out so quickly I didn't have time to consider. The power boat drew closer and the men shouted, "Doctor, you're wanted back in Baddeck right away. Kinnon Morrison is badly burned."

I transferred promptly to the McManus power boat and was back in my office within a few minutes. Kinnon was in really bad condition. I immediately gave him a quarter grain of morphine. He had extensive burns from his feet to his hips. Extensive first degree burns are the most critical. I wanted to start treating them right away with tannic acid, which was what we used for burns at that time. Then I remembered having used up the last of my tannic acid a few days before. "I have no tannic acid," I said. Jessie came through again: "Yes, doctor, you have. I saw a pound package in your drug room on the top shelf when I was cleaning in there yesterday." And the problem was solved.

During the late thirties and all through the forties, there was a steady increase in the tempo of my work. How I could have done it all without Jimmie MacIver to take care of the horses and the driving, Miss Lyttle to help on clinics and confinement cases, and Jessie Ann MacLeod to help at home, I just don't know.

By the spring of 1939, I felt I just had to have some rest and change. By this time my country practice covered a very wide area with much more than five thousand people to look after. Even with Miss Lyttle on the maternity cases I felt I had to have a vacation. But there was no doctor in the areas adjacent who had time to cover for me while still taking care of his own people.

I was very fortunate to be able to get Dr. Dan MacDonald to fill in for me, although he was 79 years of age at the time. He was well known and liked throughout the entire area. He and his wife moved into our home and my wife and I took off.

Jessie had the responsibility of looking after the home, taking care of our two young children, taking all the telephone calls, doing all the book work, and operating the x-ray machine. And because of the doctor's age, she had to help him in many other ways. That was just too much to expect one person to do, so we got Jessie's cousin, Mae Matheson, to help her. Miss Lyttle did a great deal to help Dr. MacDonald while I was away, and I had Albert Fownes, who was on vacation from medical school, to do his driving. It was the teamwork of this group of people that made possible our three-week vacation, the first real vacation we had ever had.

"There was never a dull moment during the time you and your wife were away on vacation," Jessie said. "The doctor kept us all busy waiting on him, but he was a great old scout. If the doctor had a spare moment to sit down, he would get out his violin and play Scottish jigs and reels. He often took the violin on country calls with him and played for the patients whose ills were only minor, or due to worry and care."

Jessie remembered one confinement case Dr. MacDonald handled. "The call came at three o'clock in the morning for him to go deliver Mrs. Malcolm Dauphinee on the North Shore. I went upstairs and told the doctor about it. Then I came downstairs and called the driver and the nurse to go with him. And I made a pot of coffee. While I was downstairs, the doctor was dressing but he couldn't button his shirt. I called up to Mae to get up and go in and button the doctor's shirt! They got away about four in the morning and came back about eleven. When I asked Dr. Dan how he got along with the base, he said, 'Fine. But they had ordered one big enough to do the plowing in the fall—it was a fifteen-pound boy!' "

Jessie remembered another time I went away for a few days, this time leaving Dr. Walter MacKenzie to take care of my practice. At that time there was no electricity in Baddeck, except from five o'clock in the evening until eleven. If we wanted to use the x-ray machine at other times we had to call Norman Bethune and have the electricity turned on for a minute or two. This meant we had to sterilize all the instruments in a white enamel pan on the stove in the kitchen. Jessie disliked my methods: "By the time you finished sterilizing, the kitchen would be covered with soot. You were always in a hurry, so you would take the cover off the stove and set the pan right over the coal. Then it didn't matter to you where you put the pan down—on the desk, on the chair, but wherever it was, the spot was black. And Dr. MacKenzie was just as bad or worse. When you asked me how I liked working for Dr. MacKenzie, I said I thought there was nobody worse than you, but I found out there was."

Another incident that didn't endear me to Jessie was the time she couldn't find her coal shovel to stoke the furnace one winter's morning. I had gone out on a call during the night spent a large part of it shoveling my way out of a snowbank. When I finally got back to the cold house and told of my shoveling problems, I got very little sympathy because Jessie knew right away where her coal shovel had gone.

When one is the only doctor in a large rural area, it is very difficult to get away for any reason whatever. The problem became more acute for me in 1949 when the County elected me to represent it in the provincial legislature, and kept me there for eighteen years. The normal session was eight weeks in late winter or early spring, and I would have to be in Halifax during that period. I brought in young, recently graduated doctors to look after my practice during the legislative sessions, that is, until 1962 when my son graduated and joined me in Baddeck.

Although I read the medical journals when I had time and tried to keep abreast, and had by then had a lot of experience, I found my contacts with these young men invaluable and refreshing.

And I think it fair to add that after a change of pace in looking after the political affairs of Victoria County in Halifax, I would return with renewed energy and appreciation of the people I served.

Recalling my years as the Member of the Legislative Assembly: in 1956, the party of my affiliation, the government party, was defeated, and yet, as long as I contested the seat, I was returned. I do not know whether this was because I was a good politician, a good physician, or a good neighbor. I like to think that they found in me a little bit of all three.

6

HORSES FOR WORK, FUN, AND PROFIT

I've already referred to Gypsy Queen, the little mare I bought shortly after setting up practice. She was small, but when the going was tough, without any coaxing, she put all the energy she had into her work. She served me well until I decided in 1931 to make the shift to "That Monster"—my snowmobile.

When I abandoned the snowmobile for good in 1934, I had to depend on the livery stables in town for my horses during the rest of that winter. The following year I drove a horse by the name of Norman. He belonged to Charlie MacDonald of Tarbot, who let me use him in return for his keep at the livery stable. Norman was a long-legged, rangy beast who could glide along in fairly deep snow without any effort. He was a hobbled pacer and helped provide some of the winter's entertainment in the horse races on the ice.

During the winter of 1936, I used a horse belonging to a young man by the name of MacCalder, who was working in the bank in Baddeck at the time. His home was in Orangedale, and much as he liked the horse, he felt he couldn't afford to stable him in Baddeck for the winter. We agreed that he could bring the horse to Baddeck and I would pay the horse's board at the livery stable in return for using it. If, on occasion, he wanted to use the horse himself, I would hire a horse from the stable.

One night during that winter, I was out making calls on foot in the village. MacCalder was using the horse to take a girl friend out to Big Baddeck in the sleigh—sleigh rides were a popular way to entertain young ladies in those days. Up by the Masonic Hall, I met MacCalder and the girl coming back. She was holding a handkerchief over her left cheek, holding it tightly. I could see that the handkerchief was bloody. They had overturned in a snowbank and the hard crust had torn her left cheek. When she took her hand away to show me her face, the flap of the cheek fell right down and the flap itself was well mutilated.

My first thought was that I didn't have any fine suture material in my office to do a proper job of sewing it back together. I knew I had some very fine needles, but no fine sutures. So I improvised. While their attention was drawn to my examination of her face, with my free hand I reached out and grabbed a big handful of horse hair. We went right down to the office, and I put the horsehair in a separate pan on the kitchen stove and started it boiling. I took my good time getting the wound cleaned and well frozen, giving the horsehair plenty of time to be sterilized. That horse may have gotten her into trouble, but he also provided the material to get her out of it. I saw the girl, Anna MacKenzie, years later in Halifax, and I had to look at her very closely before I could even see a scar.

The next winter, 1937, I had a little pony named Tilly, a pet, but a little light for the work. The weather wasn't bad that year, and when she got tired, I'd get a horse from the livery stable. It worked out all right, but I knew I needed a stronger horse. That year the Yacht Club needed to raise some money, so I suggested that we sell tickets on Tilly and divide the proceeds. In this way I got reimbursed for Tilly, the Club made some money, and Tilly got a good home.

The winning ticket was held by Miss Caroline MacCurdy. Miss Caroline was getting along in years by this time and we wondered if she would keep the mare. But she was so proud of winning Tilly that she kept her for many years. Her gardener, John Tommie Nicholson, used Tilly for light work on the place, hauling firewood in the winter, and the occasional sleigh drive into the village. That winter, Miss Caroline stayed on in her summer home at Baddeck Bay until some time in January so that she might have a few sleigh rides behind Tilly.

I bought Jerry Bars in the fall of 1937. He was certainly a wonderful horse; he came of racing stock, sired by Grattan Bars. Jimmie MacIver came to work for me at about that time, and he soon grew to be very fond of Jerry Bars. In fact, when I called on Jimmie a while back to ask him to help me recall some of our adventures together, the first thing he wanted to talk about was Jerry Bars and his race on the ice on March 11, 1938. The race had been planned for some time, and Jimmie was sure that he and Jerry Bars could win it.

But on the afternoon of the day before the big race, I had to take Jerry Bars out on a call to Murray MacLeod's at Upper Middle River. Jimmie worried all night that I wouldn't get back in time for the race at two o'clock the next afternoon.

The MacLeods lived in the stone house on what was then the main road to Margaree, about sixteen miles from Baddeck. I put Jerry Bars in the barn for the night, but the barn was cold and I worried that he might stiffen up and not be able to perform well the next day. The baby, Christine, was born about six-thirty the next morning and I had Jerry Bars home at nine-thirty. Jimmie gave him a good rubdown and massage and took him out for a turn or two before noon.

The race that followed is still vivid in Jimmie's mind: "Dannie MacRae and Jack MacFarlane were the official starters. They also measured out the half-mile the horses were to run. I asked them if they would do me a favor. I wanted them to add twenty or twenty-five feet on that half mile since Jerry Bars couldn't get away too fast. Our main competition was Hunter Hedgewood with a mark of 2:02½, owned and driven by Murdock W. MacRae. I got the first heat; Murdock won the second. Then I had to go back on the same track. Murdock beat me in the third heat, and I beat him in the fourth. There were two other horses in the race, Kenny MacDermid's little Bonnie L. and Danny MacLeod's Lucky B. They had finished behind us in the first four heats, so they were out of it. The fifth heat would be just Murdock and me. It was getting chilly. My arms were cold. We got away after three or four scores. They were going to call us back again but I made a sign to Jack MacFarlane to let us go. Hunter Hedgewood was just the length of himself ahead of us. I got up to his pad and just before I got to the finish I gave Jerry Bars a little touch of the whip to see how he'd do. We beat Hunter Hedgewood by a head and a neck.

"Murdock was betting a hundred dollars on his horse and Dannie MacRae was betting two hundred. That's what they say now. Other people were betting ten and twenty dollars on Hunter, and they lost it. You came along and asked how long I would be there. I told you: until I got the horse dried. You went away and when you came back you gave me fifteen dollars. My brother John Charlie gave me five dollars. It was a good day's pay for me."

I never thought Jimmie was as interested in the twenty dollars as in the fun he had racing Jerry Bars. I sent Jerry Bars to the track the following summer, 1938. In the summer the roads were open and I could answer all my calls by car. We stabled him in North Sydney and Elmer Campbell looked after him and drove him in all the races. Then we raced him in Montague, P.E.I., and in Charlottetown. He was in the money every time. When I say "in the money," in those days it was very small in comparison with today. He made his mark of 2:11½ at Montague. That fall I sent him to a track in New Brunswick, which was a mistake, because Jerry had had a hard summer of racing, and that is probably why he didn't do well in New Brunswick. We brought him home before the racing season was over.

That fall I bought Jack from Hector McRae in Middle River. Jack was a wonderful animal, a wonderful driving horse, not so handsome to look at, but he certainly could make time on the road, although he was somewhat nervous in snowbanks.

Now that I had two horses and a man to look after them, I stopped boarding them in the livery stable and moved them up to Mrs. Florrie MacPherson's barn while I was building a barn of my own. By early winter of 1939 I had my barn finished, just across the side street out my back door, in exactly the same spot where I built an office in 1962 when my son came to work with me.

My horses served me well, and we had some great adventures together. One of the first lessons I had to teach Jerry Bars was how to eat well when he had a chance. It was not an intentional lesson, but it seemed to take.

I received a call one morning to go to Angus Morrison's at Englishtown. I didn't think I'd be gone very long—it was only about eighteen miles each way. One feed of oats for "Jerry" would surely be enough. Yet when I was loading the oats into the sleigh, something told me I ought to put in two feeds for him. But then I reasoned that if there were any more calls in that area for the day, I would have heard of them by then, so I finally decided to put in just the one feed.

I arrived in Englishtown, fed my horse, had dinner with the family, and saw my patient. Just then, I got a call to Tarbot to see

Malcolm MacDonald. I reached Tarbot about five that evening. I had nothing but hay to give my horse because Malcolm was out of oats. I gave him all the hay he could eat.

Just as I was leaving Tarbot, a call came from Carmichael's at Upper Baddeck River. It would have been a heck of a drive if I'd had to go all the way by highway, twenty-five miles back to Baddeck and then another fifteen miles out to Big Glen. I knew there was a road through the woods from North Gut that would save me many miles. It was only an old wood road, but I figured I would enquire about it and use it if I possibly could.

When I reached North Gut, I found that the wood road had been used only once that winter. There had been a horse and bobsleigh through about ten days before, but it had snowed twice since then. The temptation to get through and save myself the long drive was too strong. I had that queer sensation again in the pit of my stomach when I started up the mountain between North Gut and Big Glen about midnight. The going was so heavy and so hard and so slow, I was five hours making the four-mile trip through the woods. Before I was half-way there, the horse would stop and grab the boughs of trees—fir, spruce, anything he could get he would eat. After that trip, we never had any trouble with Jerry Bars' appetite.

It was five o'clock in the morning when we reached Upper Baddeck River. I had to turn down a piece and cross the river and then go up the other side to Carmichael's. I reached there just as day was breaking, and the first thing I did was to give my horse a good feed of oats. Then I saw my patient. It was afternoon before we reached home, both pretty well tired out.

Answering the medical calls to the North Shore in the winter, ferrying my horse and sleigh at the Englishtown ferry was often complicated. In stormy weather the ferry had to be docked side on and the horse unhitched and jumped over the railing. Prior to acquiring Jerry Bars and Jack, I very often stabled my horse with Allan MacLean, the ferryman, and someone met me on the other side. Just as soon as the ice was good enough on St. Ann's Harbour I would by-pass Englishtown by taking the ice at South Gut and drive to Jersey Cove (about eight miles) on the other side of the harbor, where I stabled my horse at Donald Montgomery's.

The Montgomerys grew quite accustomed to this. One time while on the way home I arrived at the Montgomerys in the middle of the night. I didn't want to wake the family and the weather was too tough to continue on home. I suppose it was around two or three in the morning. I left my big mountain sheep fur coat on and lay down in the kitchen on a couch near the stove. The dog crawled up alongside me. When Donald Montgomery came down in the morning, he was startled at what he found on his couch. The fur coat and the dog were the same color and we must have looked like a very large animal lying there asleep.

Johnny Montgomery was a young lad at that time, but he remembers when he and his father did some doctoring for me "It was in the early thirties," he said, "and you arrived at the house sometime after supper late in the evening. Your horse had stepped in a crack going ashore and she had cut her foot. It was badly crippled. You were on a rush call down North Shore somewhere and you couldn't wait to attend to the horse. You took one of my father's horses and went right on. I remember carrying a lantern and going to the stable with my father to sew up the cut in the horse's leg. It was a lovely horse who seemed to have as much sense as we had. She held her leg real steady for the needle. You came back sometime late in the night, but you couldn't take your horse with that bad leg, so you took my father's horse back to Baddeck. A few days later someone brought our horse back, but your horse had to stay in our stable for upwards of six weeks before her leg was well."

That time stood out in Johnny's memory, but it wasn't an isolated accident. "Many another time you came to my father's. I remember one morning my father came in from the barn after feeding the horses and he asked if we had heard of anybody being sick down the shore. Nobody knew anything about it and wanted to know why he asked. He said, 'The doctor's horse is in the stable and one of ours is gone.' You used to be able to stop at my father's, leave your horse, and take a fresh one. Nobody worried about that. You'd come back sometime during the night, and you'd make yourself something to eat, and if you weren't in one of the beds asleep, you'd be catching a nap on the couch in the kitchen alongside the stove, depending on how much of a rush you were in to get back to Baddeck. Those were hard days for you, doctor."

Johnny was right. They were hard. But they would have been much harder or even impossible if it hadn't been for so many, many good people like the Montgomerys and the Murdock (Robb) MacLeods who kept a halfway house for me to help me along the way.

Both my children loved the horses and enjoyed riding them in the summer. I don't think they ever forgave me for selling Jack a few years later. I did it because he threw my daughter Connie one day. She was coming up the Bay and he suddenly went four feet up in the air, head down, and hunched his back. Connie came down and landed fair in front of a car on the highway. It happened to be Dr. and Mrs. Gilbert Grosvenor, who had been watching her and driving slowly, so they had plenty of time to stop. But the incident worried me and I didn't feel I could trust Jack any more, so I sold him back to the man from whom I had bought him.

By the end of 1949 roads had improved enough so I didn't feel I needed horses any more. I didn't have the heart to sell Jerry Bars, so I gave him to a friend who I knew would give him the best of care.

7

ORDEALS ON ICE

$\mathcal{R}$eaders who have come this far must realize that Cape Breton winter weather was the single factor that made my practice different from those of my colleagues in less isolated areas. During the summer months, when the roads were open, my practice was much like that of any country doctor in Canada in the thirties and forties. But during the winter and until late spring I had to conduct my practice the way doctors had a century earlier. I had to do without the laboratory tests, x-ray examinations, and other diagnostic tools that I had learned to rely on in medical school. And there were a great many more country calls in the bad-road season. If a person was sick enough to need a doctor, he was usually too sick to undertake the arduous trip to the doctor's office.

The Bras d'Or Lake area of Cape Breton is unique, with its bays and little points of land. Most of them are not a great distance from Baddeck. For instance, it's less than two miles to the nearest point in Washabuck, as the crow flies, but by road and across the Little Narrows Ferry it's thirty-five miles. During the first half of my years of practice, before the roads were as good or cars as plentiful, boats were used more for transportation in the summertime than they are now. But there were three to five months each year when boats could not be used because the lake was frozen. And of course, those were the same months when roads were blocked with snow drifts. In the wintertime our only physical connection with the outside world was across the ice of the Bras d'Or Lake to the Canadian National Railway, which ran from Sydney to the mainland of Nova Scotia. With so many communities in my practice situated along the shores of the lake, I had to depend on ice to get to my patients.

Good ice was my friend; bad ice was an enemy. But people became ill in these areas whether the ice was good or bad. Many times on bad ice, I thought I would never reach the shore. Some of the most frightening experiences I had were when I found myself lost during blizzards or in the fog.

I have already explained about 'bushing the ice' and that was a great help. But if the visibility was bad enough, it was easy to lose sight of the bushes. And I had to make many trips on the ice between points where there was no bushline to follow.

In January 1930 I had a call to Dan MacIvor's in South Cove. When I left home, about two in the morning, the ice was fairly good, thick enough to drive my car on, but there was heavy fog and some water on the ice in places. Three times I left Baddeck and pointed my car in what I thought was the right direction. I drove about three times the length of time it should have taken me to get to South Cove, and then came to shore. Each time I came to shore and got out to investigate where I was, I found I was behind Kidston's Island, right fair in front of Baddeck.

I finally went home and telephoned Dan. I told him I had tried to find my way across three times and couldn't make it. Dan said, "Doctor, our little boy here is very, very sick. You just have to get here." I told him to go down to the South Cove wharf and put a lantern out. That might help me some and I'd try again. On the fourth attempt, I made it. I pointed the car in the right direction, and after a while I saw a light. I followed in close but found it wasn't the light I was expecting to see on South Cove wharf. It was a light in someone's house in Washabuck. Somebody else was up that night.

However, having reached Washabuck shore, it wasn't too difficult from there. Eventually I spotted the light on the wharf at South Cove. I started to walk from the wharf to Dan MacIvor's house, which was almost a mile, and Dan met me half-way with a horse and sleigh. He had put the lantern on the wharf and gone back. When he figured I should be nearby, he came back to get me.

The little boy *was* very sick. It was a real emergency. He had a phimosis of the foreskin. He hadn't passed any water for a day or more. It was a simple operation to do a dorsal slit of the foreskin; I could have done it by myself in fifteen minutes right there in the house. But the mother was very nervous. She was just recovering from having had a baby. I hadn't been called on that case, but I knew that when the baby was two days old it had died due to bleeding from the umbilical cord. She was so nervous and upset that I didn't even suggest I do the operation on the little boy there.

Mrs. MacIvor was a half sister of the wife of Dr. Fraser MacAulay in Sydney, so we called him and arranged to take the little boy to the hospital. It was getting on toward morning, so we got the little fellow ready and Dan drove us down to the car by horse and sleigh. Mrs. MacIvor and the child got in my car and I retraced the tracks I had made coming over. I landed Mrs. MacIvor at the railway station in Shenacadie in time to catch the early morning train. She was in Sydney before nine o'clock and the little boy had his operation some time before ten. He's a strong and healthy man now. I think my time was well spent, although I had lost half the night on the ice.

One very chilling experience occurred one afternoon during the winter of 1930. I was needed at Long Hill, about six miles from Baddeck by road, but shorter if I used the ice on Baddeck Bay. I asked Neil MacKinnon to go along with me for the drive.

The ice was good, except that there had been a slight thaw a few days before and some ponds had been formed with only a couple of nights' frost covering them. When we started out, we ran into some of them. Although the horse punched through the top layer of ice, he didn't go in much above his hoofs. He'd go along a little distance, then come out of it again. Once you got into these ponds, you couldn't turn around. The sleigh cut through the ice, and you just couldn't make a circle back out of it. Down the Bay some distance we got into a deep pond, and we kept getting in deeper and deeper. I felt the only way to get out was to keep going straight ahead. I though that surely we'd start coming up out of the pond any minute. It finally got so bad the horse's belly was in the water and we were standing up on the seat of the sleigh.

Neil began to panic. He jumped over, disappeared under the top ice for a while, but then came to the surface. He was quite a tall man, but the water was up to his shoulders. He broke the ice by hand and headed for the shore. After he got on good dry ice, he was very good in giving me directions.

But there was only one thing for me to do. I couldn't turn around, so I had to get out in the water myself, break the ice by hand. I had to unhitch the horse from the sleigh, turn him around and lead him back to solid ice, and then go back and pull the sleigh out by hand. Then I rehitched the horse and headed for home as fast as I could. I was wet to my neck and had to go back home for a change of clothing before I could set out on the trip again.

There was another very cold night on the ice in March 1933. Although I had the snowmobile at that time, I had used my car to drive on the ice for a call near Little Narrows. I was on my way home about two o'clock in the morning when I burned out the clutch trying to force my way through a snowdrift near MacIvor's Point. I can still remember how cold it was that night. At that time I didn't have a heater in the car; I considered anyone with a heater in his car a bit on the soft side.

It was well below zero, and there was a wind out of the northwest. I knew I couldn't stay in my car all night; I'd be frozen before morning. I was dressed for car travel, some warm clothes, but not as many heavy clothes as I would be wearing had I expected to be exposed to the elements outside the car. I had to go somewhere to get in out of the cold.

Then on the north side of the lake I saw a light—Frank Ross's house. I knew why the light was on. About a week before I had made the first visit to see their nine-year-old daughter, Evelyn. When I first saw her, she had a definite consolidation, with pneumonia at the base of one lung. A week had now gone by and she was still very sick. I had been planning to go out to see her again the next day, so I decided to walk across the ice and make my call then. It would be a walk of about three miles, north and west, right into the face of the wind. Before I reached the house I thought for sure I was going to perish.

When I visited her recently, Mrs. Ross recalled my middle-of-the-night visit: "You had been treating Evelyn for over a week when you made that unexpected call at three o'clock in the morning. You had walked all the way across the lake and were played out and almost frozen. You had been waist-deep in snow all the way from the shore to the house, almost a quarter of a mile. Your clothes were wet and frozen on you. We got you stripped down a bit and your boots off. There was a pair of homemade wool socks hanging on the line near the stove. I remember you grabbing those socks and pulling them up on your feet. 'Nice and warm,' you said."

After I got warm enough to function, I went up to see Evelyn. I put a needle in her chest and drew off some pus. The diagnosis was empyema, and I decided to send her to City Hospital in Sydney for surgery.

Mrs. Ross remembers that they left for Sydney the next day. "The snow was very deep and the weather was very, very cold—twenty below zero at night. My husband and my uncle and I started out with two horses and two sleighs to get Evelyn across the lake and through to the train at Alba Station, a distance of about twelve miles. We had her on a cot in a box on a truck sleigh. When we got to Little Narrows, they told us that we'd never make it because of the enormous snowbanks. So my husband and uncle walked ahead of the horses, tramping down a path through the snow for them. It took us three and one-half hours from Little Narrows to Alba Station. When we got there, we put the cot on the train and the ambulance met us in Sydney and took her to City Hospital. She lived for almost two weeks after the surgery, but she passed away on March 18, 1933." It was a great shock to me, too, as I had expected she would recover with surgery.

The Ross's home had a good view of the western end of St. Patrick's Channel, as that arm of the lake is called. They often saw me driving past on the way to Nyanza or Little Narrows. Mrs. Ross remembered one night I gave them quite a scare. "One cold winter night we were sitting in our kitchen enjoying the heat from the wood stove when we noticed the lights of a car on the ice well behind Long Point. We knew it must be the doctor. Suddenly the lights went out. Somebody said, 'My God, the doctor has gone through the ice.' We didn't know what to do. We didn't want to check with his family and unnecessarily frighten them. We called Donald Smith's store in Nyanza. No one there had heard of anyone in that area being sick and sending for the doctor. They said it might just be someone out for a drive who stopped to park. An hour later someone in the store called back and said: 'The doctor is here now after walking two and a half miles on the ice. His car went through a pond in the ice.' "

I remember that night, but I didn't know at the time that the Rosses had been alarmed when "the lights went out." I remember crawling out through the window and being in water up to my waist. In struggling to get on top of solid ice, I got my clothes wet right up to my neck, but I managed to keep my medical bags dry. I can't remember, nor can anyone else, where I was heading that night or how I got home to Baddeck. I must have got through by horse and sleigh on the road. My car stayed there half submerged for a few days until the top ice was strong enough for a wrecker to go and fish it out of its hole.

I'm afraid some of the people who saw me driving on the ice sometimes had reason to doubt my good judgment. Mrs. Ross remembered another time when she and her son Aubrey were driving to Nyanza on the ice. "Down below Jeffrey's there was a bad crack running from Tony's Point across to Morris' Point. After we got around the end of the crack on the shore going in Nyanza Bay, we saw Dr. MacMillan driving on the ice. We thought the crack was impossible to get over, and that's why we had driven around the end. There was some of it peaked up in the air around ten feet; some more was low down in the water. We were watching Dr. MacMillan driving out to the crack. He drove right along the side of it and I remember Aubrey saying, 'That damn fool is going to jump that crack.' Sure enough, he went along where there was a close-looking place on the crack. He backed his car up, then at full speed ahead, he jumped it. The car went up in the air like a flying machine. He just took off. He never even stopped after he landed to look behind to see whether there was a hole there or whether it was all ice."

As I said, sometimes the ice was good and sometimes it was bad, but it was all I had to get me where I was needed. When the ice was solid, I would set out with great confidence. When I knew the ice was bad, I worried about it, but I had to use it anyway.

One such time came on March 16, 1933. Late in the evening I was called to see Angus N. MacNeil of Benacadie Pond. Mrs. A. D. H. MacKinnon, the Christmas Island telephone operator, called me to make arrangements for my trip. Often the work of several different people was required to get me to a patient. The plan we agreed upon was that I would cross the ice to Shenacadie, catch the eleven o'clock train to Christmas Island, where I would be met by a horse and sleigh to take me to Benacadie Pond, several miles back in the country.

The ice was not too good; although it was getting into late winter, it was still just salt-water ice with snow on top. I was afraid to take my car over to Shenacadie and leave it there all night, in case there should be a thaw and I would be stranded with my car across the lake, unable to get it home. So I called Freddie MacDonald who lived next door and asked if he would go with me to Shenacadie and then drive right back with my car. Freddie said yes, and we were on our way. On the way over we noticed that the ice was weak, and Freddie said he could feel the rear wheels breaking through the ice several times.

We made it across in time for me to catch the train and Freddie went back to Baddeck with my car. I took the train to Christmas Island and was met there by a young fellow with a horse and sleigh as planned. We had an hour and a half trip in the sleigh ahead of us. After a while, he asked, "Gaelic achad?" I had only a word or two in Gaelic; however, I said, "Gaelic gallore." So he started telling me a story in Gaelic. He went on for half an hour, laughing and talking in Gaelic, and having a grand time. Every once in a while I'd try to break in to tell him that I really had no Gaelic. When I finally got it across to him that he was wasting his time talking to me in Gaelic, he got so angry he wouldn't speak to me for the rest of the trip.

When I reached my patient, Angus N. MacNeil, I found that he had terminal pneumonia. I did everything I could to make him more comfortable, but I never gave the family any hope that he would recover. He died the next day.

When I had done all that I could for him, I called Freddie and asked him to drive back to Shenacadie to meet me. Freddie still remembers the trip: "About five in the morning, the doctor called and asked me to go after him. Going over I followed the track we had made the night before. I noticed many places where the wheels had punched through the ice.

"When I met the doctor in Shenacadie, we had a big discussion of how we were going to get home. We were both needed back in Baddeck, and the only way to get there was across the bad ice. Taking a chance on bad ice was not new to us. We rolled both windows down just in case the car went through and we had to get out quickly before the car sank.

"Near Baddeck we met Gerald Dunlop and his young son, Buddy, with the mail car just setting out for Shenacadie. We warned them about the bad ice but Gerald said, 'If you two got over and back, we can.' Gerald and Buddy did get back, but the mail car didn't. It is still resting on the bottom of the lake. They were lucky—and so were we."

On April 7, 1937, I lost a horse under the ice in North River, near Murray. What bothered me even more, it wasn't my own horse.

Mine was so tired that day that I left it at South Haven and borrowed Jim for the afternoon from Murdoch Rob. Jim was one of those dancing, prancing creatures, a beautiful horse, spirited and easy to drive, elegant to look at when in a sleigh. I picked up "Red" Roddie MacLeod to come along for company. I was on my way to Tarbot to give Jenny MacDonald her pneumothorax treatment for pulmonary tuberculosis. Jenny had refused to go to a sanitorium and I carried on for five years giving her this treatment every two weeks. (She is well and living in the United States, where she is doing some nursing now).

On our way to Jenny's we crossed the ice from South Gut to Murray, a distance of about five miles. The spring thaw had set in and we left the ice at Murray because we were a little afraid to go up the River. We had to walk behind the sleigh the whole of the three miles from Murray to the North River bridge. There was not one speck of snow on the ground. From the bridge to Tarbot, however, the sleighing was good.

Coming back, after giving Jenny her treatment, I had a few calls to make around North River. I called at Dan M. MacLeod's, and on leaving I told him where we were going to take the ice. He said, "If you're going to take the ice at North River, you make damn sure you get out in the middle of the harbor, because the channels are near the shore."

As we went down the river, the horse seemed determined to move in toward the shore. It was hard to keep him out in the middle. It was so foggy we could see only a few yards away. About three-quarters of the way down to Murray, the horse did get too near the shore, apparently fair over the channel. First, his two front legs went through the ice. He jumped out, and then the next time the four legs went in the ice, and he was right down in the water up to his back with just his head sticking out.

Red Roddie, who was driving, jumped out of the sleigh first, but when he hit the ice, he disappeared, and it seemed to me to be at least a minute or two before he came to the surface again. I jumped out on my side of the sleigh and ran around towards Roddie. "Don't come near me," he called. But what are you going to do when you see a man in the water and you know he can't swim? He had ice to hold onto, but a man who can't swim certainly has more fear when he gets in the water than a swimmer.

So I went up to him and tried to pull him out of the hole in the ice. Instead of pulling him out, I slipped in myself. So there we were—Roddie, myself and the horse, all in the same hole, and there we stayed, I suppose, for fifteen or twenty minutes, perhaps a half hour. Roddie got both arms around my neck and held on so tightly I couldn't get my breath. I said, "Roddie, let go of my neck and get hold of something and I'll try to get out and then get you out." I'm sure most people would have held on. Most people would have been too afraid to let go. But Roddie let go of my neck, gave a spring, although he couldn't swim, and grabbed the gooseneck of the sleigh to try to pull himself out. But instead, he pulled the sleigh in, and then we were really in trouble. He made another dive and caught the edge of the ice.

I tried to crawl out on the ice four times, and every time, just as I thought I was out, the ice would break and I'd go back in again.

It was hard to move around, dressed in heavy clothes as I was. I had on a sheepskin coat; it had the usual fastenings in front and I had added extra hooks and eyes to make the coat more windproof. Besides this, I had some brown paper stuffed inside of the front of the coat. When that coat got wet, it got heavier every minute.

When I first went in the ice, I went right down to my chin. I found, in trying to get out, that the hardest part was to getting up to the chest. Once you got that far, you could kick your feet and slide out on the ice. After the first try, when I felt myself going, I flattened myself out as much as I could and didn't go any deeper in the water. On the fifth try, I made it. I laid down and got the belt off my coat, switched the belt to Roddie, and pulled him out.

During all the time we were in the water, Roddie was doing some terrific yelling. There was a low fog on the ice and nobody could see us, but we heard people answer us and tell us they were coming. Just about two minutes before help arrived, the horse reared up and went over backwards under the ice, and drowned.

One of the first men who arrived at the scene was Dan Kennie MacLeod of North River. I got Dan Kennie in my office one day recently and asked him to give his version of what happened that day. He remembered it well: "I saw you when you went up the road on the Murray side of river in the morning. It was after that when the fog set in. In the afternoon I happened to be sitting at the door and I heard the holler, 'Horse in the ice!' I said, 'My God, the doctor is in the ice.' I ran to the barn and got a coil of rope and then ran down to the shore. It was thick fog, and I couldn't see anything but I could hear the hollering. I called, 'I'm coming,' and a voice answered, 'It's too late now. The horse is gone.' I got out there and the doctor and Roddie were there on the ice, all soaking wet. The doctor was just standing there gazing at the big hole in the ice and shivering. For a while I couldn't get a word out of him. I said,

'Boy, you better start walking. Go down to Harvey's and get in a hot tub bath.' He said, 'All right. We're going there.'

"Then I got an eel spear and a big piece of wire and I got a rope around my middle. By that time, Dan A. MacLeod and John MacGregor had come to help. They held the rope and I crawled out on the ice. I was looking down at the bottom and caught sight of two of the doctor's bags on the bottom. I was able to hook them with my wire and got the two of them up. In the meantime, the tide changed and then along came this box, the thing the doctor used for giving gas. That floated up on the water, so I got that ashore, too. There was no sign of anything else. I took the bags and the box home with me."

But that wasn't the end of the story. Dan remembers going back the next day after the fog had cleared and the tide changed again. "The horse and the sleigh were floating there in this big hole. I took a boat, dragged it across the ice with John MacGregor's help, and we launched it in the hole. I took the sleigh off the horse and pulled it out on the ice. Then I took the harness off the horse and saved that. I said, 'When the channel opens in a few days, boy, you'll go out to sea.' I took the harness and sleigh home, and the buffalo robe, too. That was still in the sleigh. In a day or two, the ice broke up and the channel went right down. Then the channel broke on my side, so there were two channels leading out toward the sea. What did Mr. Horse do but float right up the channel on my side of the river and came ashore there. We had to go down and take that horse and haul him in as far as we could during low tide. We dug a big hole down in the mud, cut the legs and head off, so the hole wouldn't have to be too big, and we buried him there. And that was the end of that trip."

It was the end for him, but not for me. Although I realized that Murdoch, the horse's owner, would already have heard the bad news, I dreaded meeting him when I got back to South Haven. I told him, "You go to the country, anywhere at all, and get the very best horse you can find. Let me know what the bill is and I'll pay." But the horse he got was never the same as the one I lost that day in the ice. He was a good driver, all right, but not the same kind of horse material that Jim had been.

It was always a good idea when taking to the ice, particularly at night or during a storm or fog, to have another person along. Fortunately I rarely had trouble finding someone to go with me, no matter how bad the weather or how dangerous the ice.

Ralph Pinaud was one of those who frequently accompanied me. I've already related some of our adventures in the snowmobile. Recently he reminded me of a couple of other incidents, one of which I had almost forgotten.

"I was eating supper one evening in 1937 down at my father's house, when I heard a horn blowing out in front on the ice. I went out to see who it was and found Dr. MacMillan, who wanted me to go for a 'short drive' with him. I got into warm clothes and away we went. I asked him where he was going and he said 'up the shore.' The ice was so bad many places we had to go ashore to get by the wide-open cracks. After passing Sand Point, the doctor headed out across the lake. The ice looked black to me and not very safe. I asked again, 'Where are we going?' and this time he told me we were heading for South Cove. That meant we had to cross the lake. His 'little drive' was getting longer and longer.

"The going wasn't too bad until we got close to the shore. About five times the rear wheels of the car went down through the ice. The running boards cars had in those days stuck out like fins and would keep the car up until she'd pick up and go. When we landed on the shore I said to the doctor, 'I believe the ice was gone back there.' We decided to go back and have a look. We took a shovel and poked it in the wheel tracks. There was no ice, only open water. We decided then that the ice wasn't fit to go back on, so we kept up on the shore for a short piece until we found more solid ice, and then headed out on the lake again. After a few miles we came ashore at Hazeldale.

"From there, we had to walk through deep snow to Ivor MacIvor's, about half a mile. The doctor went in and pulled a tooth for Ivor, and then we had the problem of getting home. We decided to go by way of Nyanza, where we thought the ice would be better.

"It was a very dark night and we couldn't pick out any landmarks. After about ten minutes of driving, I asked the doctor to stop the car and let me get out and look. I hadn't walked a hundred feet and there in front of me was the mouth of Middle River, wide open water."

I remember telling Ralph, "At least we know where we are now." He crawled back in the car and we started off again. I turned my lights out so I could see the outline of the hills to guide me, and turned right, timed the driving carefully, and then turned left, which brought me ashore near Gordon MacIver's store. The road to Baddeck had many mud holes, but we made it back before morning.

If bad ice was a threat, good ice was a boon. It helped me make a record trip in March 1935. Mary Harrington, a young girl who lived on the mountainside in West Middle River, had been in a coasting accident. I was needed in a hurry. The call came just after a heavy snowstorm and blizzard. The roads had not yet been broken, and

I knew no driving horse would get through the snowbanks that day. It was while I was in the barn harnessing Norman that I realized the only hope of getting through to her that day was to take the ice up the lake, a fifteen-mile trip.

I went on the ice at the club house, got by the bad crack at Sand Point on the seawall without any mishap, passed Morris's Point, and came ashore near the Indian village. It wasn't too far by road from there. When I arrived at Mary's house, her parents told me that it was just forty-five minutes since they had phoned.

I put Mary on the kitchen table and started sewing. It wasn't a cut; it was a tear and required a lot of stitching. The flesh was ripped on the upper part of the leg and the lower part of the abdomen. When I was doing the suturing I could see the inner lining of the abdominal cavity. I think I was busy for probably three-quarters of an hour on that job; Mary said the local anesthesia was beginning to wear off before I was through. Before we got the hospital in Baddeck, all this sort of work was done in the home. It never occurred to us to send a patient to the Sydney or North Sydney Hospital for this type of thing. To get a patient to the hospital would have taken a day or more and would have been a great hardship on the patient. Better to go to work on it and get it done right away.

Good ice more than once helped me save a life. And if there are fewer stories here about good ice, that's because a trip on good ice was just a routine matter that I easily forgot, while a trip on bad ice always impressed itself on my mind.

The ice was an indispensable help the night Carmen MacInnis was born. Neilie MacInnis called me at two in the morning, and I started out right away for their home in South Cove. The ice was in perfect condition. By four in the morning I had been across the ice, delivered the child, and was back home in bed. And this despite the fact that there were complications that might have been disastrous for the baby.

The minute the head slipped down in the pelvis, I discovered the umbilical cord was short. There were two twists around the neck, and the cord had tightened up so much that there was no pulsation whatever in it. Before the baby was born, I used two clamps, clamped the cord and then cut it. I couldn't wait on nature now. I had to use instruments to deliver the baby immediately. The whole procedure took less than two minutes. There was a considerable amount of mucus in the chest, but some breathing. I spent ten or fifteen minutes getting the infant's chest clear of mucus, and by the time I left I was quite satisfied that the baby would be all right.

Mrs. MacInnis told me that night that I was in her house within eleven minutes of the time she called me. If I had to make the trip by horse and sleigh, all the way around Little Narrows, I couldn't have done it in less than seven or eight hours. The baby wouldn't have survived.

The following morning I went back again to check on the baby. I called before I left home and Mrs. MacInnis claims I was in her house nine minutes after I called. It would be about nine miles. This was the only trip I can remember making to South Cove under good traveling conditions.

Sometimes conditions were such that a boat could be used for part of a trip. Then I would have to switch to sleigh for another leg of the distance and then get out and walk across ice that wouldn't support a horse and sleigh. It was a tricky business figuring out just how to get somewhere and home again.

Stephen R. MacNeil of Barra Glen remembers just such an incident: "It was the time Tina was born. That would be January 29, 1940. I met you on the morning boat at Irma with horse and sleigh. Although the mail boat was still operating between Baddeck and Iona, a few miles west of Baddeck the lake was frozen all the way across. You asked me at Iona if you were not through at my place in time to catch the afternoon boat, would it be possible for me to drive you to South Cove."

I was expecting a call down to Goose Cove, which might have come at any minute. I wanted him to drive me to South Cove so I could walk the ice to the north side of the lake.

"You didn't get through here until about midnight. It was raining very hard, a strong wind, and no visibility. Still, I was willing to go. I had the horse ready. But when you looked out you said, 'I don't think I'll risk it; and you stayed here that night." The risk was in walking that kind of ice at night in that kind of weather.

I'm glad to have his testimony that I had good sense about ice at least once in a while. We started out at daybreak, which made walking the ice a little safer. It was possible to see the ponds and avoid them, or at least decide which ponds were safe to cross. You can judge the depth of the pond by the color of the water and the size of the waves. Above all, it is important to stay away from dry spots on the ice. Ice that won't hold water is not safe.

As I said, we left at daybreak and I expected to get home by nine o'clock, but it was noon before we reached South Cove. The horse had to plunge through soft snow all the way. I spent the afternoon snaking my way across the ice around ponds and dry areas. It was dark before I reached home. As I was entering my office, the phone was ringing. It was the call to Goose Cove I had been expecting.

Not all of my hard experiences on the ice were in the vicinity of Baddeck, or between Baddeck and Washabuck, though it sometimes seemed to me as though the ice in that section was a personal enemy. The people of the county knew well the difficulties and hazards of winter travel. They were always appreciative of the efforts expended to reach them, and reciprocated by giving a hand in helping me reach or treat others.

Mrs. Malcolm MacDonald of Upper Washabuck summed up the attitude of most of my patients when she said recently: "I've lived here for thirty-four years, and in my day we've had new babies, small children, and for a number of years we had the old and the ailing in our home. It was only normal that there would be periods of stress and anxiety, worry, pain, and suffering. We always sent for Dr. MacMillan. Very often he would be down at the far end of the county, but somehow or other, the message always got through to him and he came. But it wasn't just 'plain coming.' It wasn't all that easy. Sometimes he was in snow to his ears and at other times he could have been in mud to the axle, because we were always blessed with very poor roads. Sometimes on his trips to this area, he'd cross the ice on the lake, and sometimes he took a ducking into the icy water of the Bras d'Or. How he ever survived, heaven only knows."

She remembered that as recently as twenty years ago, when her youngest child was born, winter travel was still a problem. Though the roads had been improved and snowplows were used widely enough so that I had given up the use of horse and sleigh, I had trouble reaching her home to deliver the baby. Along the way the snow on the road had become very soft and my car sank right into it. I was there for quite a while, shoveling and trying to ram my way out of it, before someone came along and pulled me out. I made it to her home then under my own power and arrived in time to take care of the delivery.

A few years before that Mrs. MacDonald had helped me on a confinement case in her neighborhood. The birth was not an easy one, and I had to return to Baddeck to get some equipment I had not taken with me. Mrs. MacDonald recalls watching my return trip across the ice: "On his way back to Washabuck, the ice had been melting and the people on this side could just see a spray of water coming from the wheels of the car as he drove along. While he was away, I was very, very nervous, afraid that the child would be born while he was gone and I wouldn't know very well what to do, but he assured me before he left that nothing would happen in a hurry."

I must add here that when I assured Mrs. MacDonald I'd be back, I had my fingers crossed. You had to know exactly where you were going on the ice. I didn't tell her I was afraid I would go to the bottom of the lake myself that day.

When Mrs. MacDonald returned to her own family that night, she was just in time to help at the birthing of the first lamb of the season. "I was so keyed up after my day in the 'maternity ward' I was unable to sleep all that night."

It was always reassuring to me to know that people all along the way were concerned about my whereabouts when I was out in bad weather. I'm afraid some of them did a lot of worrying on my behalf. One such occasion was on February 24, 1950, at the height of a blizzard.

About one o'clock in the morning I was called to John R. MacNeil's at Barra Glen to attend his wife during confinement. The road around through Little Narrows was blocked by snow. John R. said if I could get across to Washabuck on the ice by car, he would get the snowplow operator to keep the road open from Washabuck to his gate, where he would meet me with horse and sleigh.

At that time I had a jeep. I woke Jimmie MacIvor up and asked him to come with me. In a very short time we were on our way.

Francis (Michael D.) MacNeil, who was the snowplow operator for the Washabuck road at that time, recalled, "I waited down at the shore at Washabuck Center and, oh boy, it was cold, dark, and blowing hard. I covered the road all night, keeping it clear all the way to John R.'s gate. In the morning, when it got light, I went down to Francis MacDonald's to telephone Baddeck. I found out that the doctor and Jimmie had left Baddeck shortly after getting the call and had not been heard from since."

John R. was worried, too. He was at his gate to meet me at the appointed time, but I didn't show up. There was considerable loose snow down and he thought I might be stuck somewhere between Barra Glen and the shore. He drove down to the end of the Barra Glen road, but there was still no sign of me. It was bitterly cold and a terrific strong wind blowing from the northwest. He said, "I waited and waited at the end of the road, but still no doctor. The wind was so strong that I really thought that the horse and sleigh would be blown into the lake. I was so cold by that time, I was frozen. So I went into Malcolm Dan MacNeil's home and telephoned Baddeck. I learned the doctor had left shortly after one o'clock. Then I telephoned Washabuck to find out if anyone had seen a car crossing the ice. No one had seen or heard any sign of a car crossing. I decided the doctor must have changed his mind and was trying to get through around the end of the lake by car, so I went home."

Where was I in the meantime? Jimmie and I got in the jeep and started up the lake. We tried to cross the crack that runs between Pinaud's Yacht Yard and Kidston's Island. We got one wheel in the crack. It didn't take us very long to get out, perhaps half an hour, and then we had to turn back. I was a little afraid at the time to go out behind the island. With the clean sweep of the wind, there would be a lot of drifting snow and snowbanks here and there on the ice. At night one wouldn't be able to see them in time to avoid them.

I then decided to go up the shore to find a place where I could get on the ice. My intention was to cut right across to Washabuck, but in trying to make the ice from the road, we got stuck in the snow. Jimmie and I had two shovels. I don't know how long we were getting out, but we never made the ice there.

We finally came back to Baddeck and again took the ice. This time, we went out behind the island. I got up all the speed I could, to get through the short banks on the ice, and we made it up as far as John Paul MacLean's. There we stuck solid. We couldn't move and there was nothing else to do but walk ashore.

Paul MacLean remembers that night, too. "That night was one of the coldest that winter, about fifteen below zero and with a high wind. I heard a knock on the door around five o'clock in the morning. I went down and it was Dr. MacMillan and little Jimmie MacIvor. The doctor was heading for Iona on a confinement case.

"He told us he had left town about one and had been shoveling snow all night. He had been on the way for four hours and only made it to our house, a distance of two miles. He asked if I could take him over the rest of the way to Barra Glen. It was drifting so badly I said we had better wait until daylight. The comical part of it was the doctor said the wind was so high he was afraid he was going to lose little Jimmie between the car and our house and he knew he'd never make the people of Baddeck believe that when he got back. But in spite of his joking, the doctor really wanted us to start out right then. It was fifteen below zero and the wind was gusting up to sixty miles an hour. I told him I would take him when daylight came. But he just said, 'I'll go walking,' and he left the house. He wasn't gone but about fifteen minutes when he came back again. He had decided to wait for morning."

The reason I was so impatient was that the patient, Mrs. John R. MacNeil, or "Betty Red Rory" as we called her, had now been in labor quite a while. Her first confinement had been a long, hard case. I was hoping this present one would be a case of a long labor, too, but I couldn't count on it.

Paul MacLean remembers it as a hard trip, even after daylight: "We got across by car from our place. We were in Barra Glen by around nine o'clock in the morning. We had quite a distance to walk to Betty Red Rory's house from the main road, almost three-quarters of a mile. With the bitter cold and the hard wind, our ears and faces were frozen before we reached the house."

It was a night of worry for Betty Red Rory, too. She not only had to worry about where the doctor had disappeared to, but whether he would turn up in time to take care of her delivery. "We sent for the doctor about midnight," she said. "I thought perhaps if we waited a while the storm might ease, but instead of that it was getting worse. We had no telephone and we went out and called from a neighbor's house. Then we waited and waited all night for him to come. The baby was born at seven and the doctor didn't arrive until nine. Everything was all right when he got here, but we were sure glad to see Dr. MacMillan walking in on that cold, stormy morning."

The spring of the year usually produced the most difficult travel conditions because the ice went bad before the roads became good.

On April 4, 1941, I was called to the Malcolm Dan MacNeil home at Grass Cove. The ice from Baddeck to Washabuck was too thin to carry a person walking, let alone a horse and sleigh. And the road was impassable. The ice four miles up the shore, from Dan Hutchison's house to Washabuck, had formed much earlier, and I thought, with a little luck, I might be able to cross there on foot. I told Malcolm Dan I would try this route and asked him to meet me at the shore in Washabuck Center, near the church. Then I called Dan Hutchison on the telephone and asked what he thought about the ice in front of his house. He didn't give me much encouragement. "It's a dark night and there are too many holes in the ice," he said. However he volunteered to walk the ice with me if he could get someone else to go along.

When I arrived at Dan's, he had Dave Munroe with him and they were ready to start. With long rope, Dan tied the three of us together, each about ten feet apart. It was 10:30 by my watch when we left the shore. Every few steps Dan tested the ice with his ax. If the ax went through with a light tap, he'd start us in another direction. We were not much more than an hour getting to the Washabuck shore, where I found Malcolm Dan waiting. I wasn't there too long; I was on my way back home long before daylight. Stephen (Jim) MacNeil drove me back over the mountain to Washabuck.

I knew Stephen Jim quite well. He used to have a big gray horse that he drove in some of our winter races. He always used a riding sleigh. The big gray didn't come from racing stock, but I always thought if that horse had been in a bike and had a little training, he would have cleaned up on the rest of us.

That night coming back, it turned quite cold. Stephen Jim had brought a little bottle with him to take a little sip now and then to keep him warmed up. I asked him what it was and he offered me some. I took a mouthful. It was raw. That's the way all Cape Bretoners liked their drink a few years back. It was a good thing he had it, though, because by the time we got to Neil Stephen MacLean's at Washabuck Center, I decided that, since it had been such a cold and frosty night, I'd walk the ice alone.

It was about five in the morning by this time and still dark. When I told Stephen Jim that I would walk over alone he said, "No, you won't," and turned his horse in at the MacLean home. He drove right into the yard and rapped on the door with his whip butt, waking them. I had a few hours' sleep, then at about nine o'clock I took a short-cut through the woods down to the ice near the church and walked across alone.

Johnny Hutchison, Dan's oldest son, tells me now they were watching me that morning when I was walking back. He says I wandered too far to the east and walked over a stretch of ice that had been open water the day before. A little light snow had fallen during the night. I was totally unaware that I had walked over about fifty feet of ice that was less than two inches thick, with not a worry in the world.

8

ACCIDENTS HAPPEN

ccidents happen. And unfortunately they often happen at very inconvenient times and places. Now, of course, with our fine modern roads, plentiful cars, and planes and helicopters available to transport patients from remote areas, most accident victims can be treated in well-equipped emergency rooms. But it wasn't that way during the early years of my practice. The doctor had to get to the patient as fast as he could, and that was often a real problem. Then he had to treat the patient using only the tools and supplies he carried in his bag. Occasionally an accident victim might be brought to my office, if the accident had occurred nearby, but most often I had to grab my bags and run.

One big problem back in the days before the use of shatterproof glass in automobiles was the number of injuries that resulted from every car accident. Car accidents then weren't as common as they are now, but if there was a car accident at all, everybody involved was badly cut. One time during the first year I was in Baddeck I had six people lying on the floor of my office, waiting to be sutured. It was at least three or four hours before I attended them all. It was quite common to put fifty or sixty stitches around the head, neck, and face of such victims.

Of course, over the years I attended many accident victims where the damage was more serious than cuts from flying glass. One such accident occurred on July 18, 1952. I received a call to go to Iona. It was such a beautiful day that my wife went along with me for the drive, and just before leaving, I put my fishing gear in the car. I thought that, after making my call, I might spend perhaps a half hour or so fishing at a brook somewhere on the way home.

On our return trip we turned in Fisher's Road (as we used to call it—it's now called Campbell Road) up near Portage. I parked the car, changed into my fishing clothes, put my rod together, put a Par Bell fly on, and then started down the marsh to Fisher's Brook. My wife had a book with her and planned to spend the time reading while I fished.

I was about half way to the brook when all of a sudden I stopped short. I turned back to the car, tore off my boots, changed from my fishing clothes into my regular clothing, got into the car, and drove like mad for home.

My startled wife said, "Daddy, what in the world is wrong with you?"

"There's going to be a bad accident in Baddeck and I want to get there before it happens." She thought I was crazy.

When we reached home, everything was quiet. But before I had been there ten minutes I got an emergency call to Baddeck Bay. A car had gone off the road and rolled over the bank. A man named Buddy Auld was seriously injured.

After a quick examination at the scene of the accident, we moved the patient to the hospital. He had cerebral concussion, severe lacerations around the nose, fracture of ribs along the left chest, some left kidney damage, and was in shock. We gave him a hypo of morphine, sutured his lacerations, and strapped up his chest.

It was only then I thought about the premonition I had had only an hour earlier. It frightened me. I remembered as I was walking down to the brook I had a guilty feeling. I was taking time off and no one knew where I was. If I were needed, no one would know where to look. I tried to rationalize the situation. Everything was under control when I left home, and there was no maternity case due. But I still felt guilty. What if there should be an accident? The more I thought about it, the more an imminent accident became a reality. But I wondered then and I've wondered since whether I do indeed have a "sixth sense." If so, I wish it had put itself to work as a direction finder during some of those dark nights on the ice!

However that may be, the fact is that I was at home to take care of Buddy Auld when the call came. A couple of days later he had some soreness in the abdomen, which was only to be expected. On July 21, three days after the accident, he was feeling better and he remarked to me, "Doctor, I think I'm well enough to go home today." Up to that time he had been confined to bed completely. But I wasn't satisfied. There was a little fullness in the abdomen, which I had been attributing to the broken ribs. It is quite common to get soreness in the abdomen when you have three or four broken ribs, particularly near the front end of the chest.

It was about five o'clock the next morning when the hospital called me. The two nurses on duty that night were Miss Margaret MacLeod, a Registered Nurse, and Miss Donna King, a nursing attendant. When Buddy's buzzer sounded, Donna answered, took one look at the patient and called Margaret. He was in shock, delirious, and trying to get out of bed to go to the washroom. They had some difficulty in controlling him, but finally satisfied him by putting him on the bedpan, and then they called me.

When I reached the hospital and put my hand on Buddy's abdomen, I knew something had gone wrong there. The most likely probability was a massive hemorrhage. His hemoglobin, which was all right when he first went into the hospital, had dropped to 45 per cent.

I administered a quarter-grain of morphine and immediately started what we called "artificial blood." Then, very shortly thereafter, I got blood from Sydney, Group O RH negative, which we could use in an emergency case. We took a sample of Buddy's own blood and had a second quantity of that delivered. I can't remember just how we got the blood up from Sydney or North Sydney, but I remember that it came quickly. We didn't have a blood bank in Baddeck.

Buddy told me the name of his family doctor in Sydney, Dr. Abie Gaum. I called him, and told him the story, explaining what I had done. By this time we had Buddy in pretty good shape. We had two or three pints of blood into him, plus plasma and some blood expander, and I felt he was quite ready for surgery. I told Dr. Gaum that I was afraid to move Buddy or to put him in a car to move him to Sydney, afraid of what would happen before he reached the hospital.

Dr. Gaum came to Baddeck and brought with him his head operating room nurse, and Dr. Giovanetti to give the anesthesia. I assisted. We never did major surgery in our hospital, and I believe Buddy Auld is the only person to have had his abdomen opened there. We found Buddy's belly full of blood, the source of which was the spleen. It was completely crushed. Dr. Gaum removed it. How Buddy lived four or five days with all the trouble he had is hard to imagine.

Buddy had a very uneventful recovery. The operation was performed on July 22, and on July 31 he was discharged from the hospital. He didn't go home by ambulance either; he went by car. He was driving his own car two weeks from the day of the accident.

In our area, frequent accident victims were the loggers, working way back in the mountains. On July 5, 1929, I received what was the first of many calls to the lumber woods, some miles in the mountains back of North River. Roddie Morrison was badly cut. A doctor was urgently needed. Roddie's brother Duncan remembers the accident: "I was working in the woods near him that morning and the first thing we had to do was to strap him on horseback and, leaving a trail of blood all the way, take him seven miles to camp number nine, the base camp."

To reach him at camp number nine, I drove twenty-three miles to North River Bridge, seven miles to the top of the mountain, and transferred there to a horse and wagon for eight miles over a corduroy road. When I examined the patient I found that Roddie had driven an ax almost through one foot. When we removed the boot it looked as though most of the foot was going to come with it. The ax had severed all the tendons and blood vessels on the top of the foot, and had cut through all the bones. There was some flesh left on the underpart with the circulation intact.

The bleeding came under control when I stuck the foot back in place and bandaged it there. We put him in the wagon, elevating his foot by fixing it to the top of the dashboard. The driver kept one arm around Roddie so he wouldn't fall out; Roddie was weak from loss of blood and the corduroy road was very rough. I walked behind the wagon. When we reached my car, we transferred Roddie to it, still with the leg elevated, and took off for North Sydney Hospital.

The operating room was all set up and the surgeon, Dr. L. R. Meech, was waiting for us. We were more than two hours in the operating room, but it was time very well spent. I'm happy to report that in due time Roddie walked without any disability.

A year later, at the same time of year, I was called to camp seventeen to see a man with exactly the same kind of injury. This time the victim was Calvin Shaw. It was nearly midnight when I reached the camp, and at first I thought I might be able to handle the case right there. But when I got a flashlight out and gave it a second examination and saw all the damage that was done, I decided he had to go to the hospital. Calvin was bleeding profusely. I put a tourniquet around his thigh and we loaded him on the wagon. I walked behind the wagon the entire seven miles out to the top of the mountain. The trip out to the road was very slow, because every once in a while I would stop to loosen the tourniquet and let a little blood through. It was four in the morning when we reached the car. By that time there was enough clotting, so I removed the tourniquet.

Driving down Boulardarie, near Big Bras d'Or, I fell asleep at the wheel. The first thing I knew, the patient was pounding me in the ribs with his elbow, trying to wake me. There I was driving about fifty miles an hour on an old country road, with both wheels on one side in the ditch, and sound asleep.

At the hospital, Dr. Meech was again the surgeon, and we were two and a half hours in the operating room. It was near noontime before I started for home. Halfway up Boulardarie I distinctly remember that all of a sudden I didn't know who I was. I didn't seem to know anything. All I *did* realize was that each car I passed seemed to be getting a little closer; then I saw a car heading right for me. It was with great effort I pulled the car to my side of the road and stopped. I got out and wandered around for some time before I woke up.

I recall another accident involving an ax, but this time the victim was a young boy. Alex Kerr of North River reminded me of this one: "Back in January 1937 my brother and two or three other kids were out skating. My brother climbed up on a clamper of ice to get some birch bark from a tree. We were going to make a fire. He threw the ax back down on the ice and he started to climb down himself and slipped. It was one of those double axes. The ax stuck in the ice and when he came down, he fell on the other blade. He split the palm of his hand and up across his wrist. This happened, I suppose about nine or ten o'clock at night. We went right home and my father called the doctor. He drove right down, using the ice from South Gut to North River. My father met him there with the sleigh.

"There was another man there at the time by the name of Donald MacDonald, better known as 'Donald Garrett.' He held the light as the doctor was operating. Some of the cords had been cut, so the doctor had quite a job. After a while, Donald couldn't stand it any longer and he had to get someone else to hold the light. He had to go outside and throw up."

Alex also remembered that there had been some concern about how I would get home that night. About midnight his father took me back to my car, but the snow was deep all around and there was no place to turn around. As Alex tells the story, I saw a place where the sheep had been milling around in the snow and had flattened it down. "He wiggled the car around in this place and away he went back to Baddeck."

Colin Nicholson's accident was a different sort: His horse kicked him and broke three ribs. It happened on New Year's Eve when my wife and I were at a square dance in the Masonic Hall. About eleven o'clock I got word by messenger from the telephone office that I was wanted at Nicholson's house. The road was very icy that night and I was in a hurry because I wanted to get back to the dance. I was stepping on the gas. At the top of the hill, just before the Red Bridge, my car began to skid and turned end-for-end two or three times, finally coming to a stop crossways at the end of the bridge, completely blocking the bridge. I finished the trip on foot.

Colin remembered the night: "As so often happened, the doctor finished his trip out here by walking. He had a big fur coat on, which he took off and threw on the fence at Seaward MacRae's before walking the last two miles. It was too heavy and too warm to be walking in."

When I returned to my car later, I found that someone had driven it off the bridge and parked it nicely on the side of the road, headed back toward Baddeck. I never found out who did it, but I was grateful.

Another accident that stands out in my memory occurred in July of 1933. I was called to go to "Lame Dan" Morrison's at Upper Baddeck River. He had no telephone in his home, so the message came to me by messenger from the nearest telephone. The person who called didn't tell me what the accident was, but said I was needed immediately out at Lame Dan's and to get there as fast as I could because Mrs. Morrison was badly hurt. Mrs. Morrison was well into her seventies.

To reach Lame Dan's I drove out past the home of John Dan MacKay, the mail driver, and then turned across the river. I drove up through Christopher MacLeod's farm, where they were haymaking. Then I turned into a back road, getting out two or three times to open gates. That part of the country was all farmland then; it's all wilderness now.

When I got to Lame Dan's I found that Mrs. Morrison really needed me. That morning there had been some neighboring boys in visiting the Morrisons. The boys were playing with the Morrison's dog, a Scotch collie, that had been a perfectly well-behaved pet for many years. The boys wrapped a piece of rope around the dog's nose, probably cutting his wind off.

Then in the afternoon, Mrs. Morrison decided to visit the neighbors, and because she didn't want the dog to follow her, she decided to tie it up before she left home. She picked up the same piece of rope that the boys had used in the morning and started towards the dog. As she did, the dog attacked her.

Another neighbor, Phillip MacLean happened to be going by the house just at this time and he heard some kind of racket going on, so he went in to investigate. He had to kill the dog with an ax before he could stop the dog's attack on Mrs. Morrison.

When I examined her I found so many tears I gave up trying to count them. She was chewed up from head to foot, some of the tears quite deep in the flesh. I started out by suturing up a few of the tears and leaving one corner open in case of infection. However, after a while I decided to give them all a good washing with soap and water and just bandage her up. I wrapped her up like a mummy, put her to bed, and got some of the neighbors in to look after her. I don't think she stayed in bed very long, because I know that in less than two weeks she was around doing all her own work again. Every wound healed without any infection whatsoever, and she lived for several years after that.

The hunting season often produced its own sort of accident. I remember being called to MacKinnon Harbour on December 3, 1949, to treat a hunter who had been shot in the leg. Just why I didn't go by road I can't say now, but I suppose I figured that the roads would be blocked with snow. Anyway, the arrangement was that the Washabuck ferry would be sent over for me and a car would meet me on the other side. If I could have traveled by road, I would have been there in not much more than half an hour and would have been much more comfortable.

The Washabuck "ferry" was a small open boat. The wind that night was out of the northwest and heavy. About three-quarters of the way across the lake, the engine conked out. We drifted for some time while the men fooled around with the engine. They even got oars out and tried to row, but the wind and high seas prevented any progress. Our only hope then was that the boat would drift in to shore near MacKay's Point. Beyond that there was nothing but open water. However, it became evident that we weren't going to hit MacKay's Point but would pass about a hundred yards from the shore. For a while it looked as though we would spend a night on the water, drifting in a small motor boat.

But then one of the boys felt the gas line and found one very cold spot in it. Perhaps the trouble could be a bit of ice in the line at that spot. One of them said, "Boys, I think we'll all have to urinate on that spot in the line." (I'm using a word that's a little more acceptable and polite than the one he used, but it means the same thing.) Immediately, the first one started, and then the second one. Then they said, "Doctor, it's your turn." This did the trick. They gave the engine another turn, and away we went.

At Washabuck we found the car that had been waiting there for the two hours we were drifting around the lake. Soon I was with the patient. I found that the high-powered rifle had shattered the femur, and, I thought, the main artery to the leg. He wasn't a native of the area, but from one of the towns to the south of us. I made him as comfortable as possible with a shot of morphine, settled him into his own car, and one of his buddies drove him as they set off for their own hospital. There was nothing more I could do for him there. I learned later that when they got to Grand Narrows ferry that night, they were unable to wake the ferryman. At that time, when you needed the ferry at night, you used the telephone and it rang at the man's home. But that night he was sleeping too soundly. Finally somebody had to walk the Grand Narrows railway bridge and wake him up.

9

OTHER EMERGENCIES

What is an emergency in general practice? I define it as a situation when immediate action must be taken to preserve life or limb. Often the only part the general practitioner has in it is to make a diagnosis if possible, perhaps administer some sedative, and see that the patient is properly transported to the nearest medical center.

Early in the afternoon of a day in March 1931, I got a call from Mrs. Archie Fraser, the wife of the minister at North River. Their baby boy, Lloyd, a year and a half old, had swallowed a mixture of lye and soapsuds that she had on the pantry shelf. He had climbed up on the pantry shelves, found the dish with the mixture, and started to drink it before she could grab him. He got at least some of it in his throat. She said she had had a terrific time with the child for a while, getting his mouth washed out. The baby choked and gasped, but at the time she called me she seemed to think he was all right. She just wasn't sure whether any lye had gone down his throat or not.

The weather was clear, but there had just been a heavy snowfall, and I knew it would take me some hours to get down there. Mrs. Fraser didn't seem too worried about the child at the time she called. I instructed her to mix some vinegar and water and give him a little drink of that once in a while in case there was some of the lye mixture in his stomach, and to let me know how he was a little later in the afternoon.

About two hours later she phoned and told me to come as fast as I could. The child was having trouble breathing.

We arranged that she would send a heavy horse to meet me halfway, so I drove my mare quite hard knowing that I would be able to put her up at South Gut. The boy's father, Reverend Archie Fraser, had been down at Wreck Cove when he received word about the child. Apparently he wasn't notified until they realized that the baby was really sick. He was back in North River a couple of hours before I arrived. It took me seven hours to travel the twenty-three miles from Baddeck; I got there about midnight. I can still remember that trip. Maggie MacQueen, who operated the Telephone Office at South Gut, used the party-line system to keep people informed every step I took with the horse from the time I left Baddeck until I reached South Gut. There I was met by the horse sent from North River, and again Maggie kept track of my progress with calls from each house I passed. It was a really heavy horse that took me through some deep snow-banks, but not a real driving horse.

As soon as I got in the house I could hear the young child upstairs breathing. I was shivering and shaking so badly from the cold I knew I couldn't do anything until I got warm. So I spent a few minutes at the kitchen stove with my feet in the oven. I knew by the sound of the baby's breathing that he had an inflammatory condition of the glottis, which was closing off the air passages. While I was getting warm, I removed my scalpel from my bag, a couple of pairs of artery forceps, and some suture material, all of which I put in the little enamel dish I carried for this purpose. Then I poured some antiseptic solution over them, just in case I had to do a tracheotomy. By the time I was warm enough to stop shaking, the instruments were sterile.

When I went up to examine the baby, I found he was conscious but breathing with great difficulty. He was in his parents' arms. Mr. Fraser remembers, "You said to lay him down, that there wasn't a thing we could do. I had the feeling that something was going to happen that would help him. So I told the doctor that if there was anything he could do that might help, go ahead and do it."

There was certainly indication for a tracheotomy. It was only with great effort that the child was able to get any air through to the lungs. He had rales in both lungs from top to bottom, and I diagnosed a chemical pneumonia as well. I got them to lay the baby down with the idea of attempting a tracheotomy, but then I'd look at the baby and I'd look at the knife. He seemed so small. I certainly didn't want to do a tracheotomy if I could avoid it. Perhaps I lacked courage.

Anyway I decided I would postpone the tracheotomy for a while. I gave the baby one six-hundredth of a grain of atropine by needle, attempted some steam inhalation, and some medication by mouth to counteract the corrosion in case some of the lye had reached his stomach. Then I waited an hour.

There seemed to be a slight improvement. I repeated the atropine and waited another hour. Again there seemed to be improvement. I injected the one six-hundredth grain of atropine every hour from twelve that night until noon the next day. After two or three hours the baby could get enough air so that he could sleep. By noon the next day I was satisfied that the baby had a chance of recovering and I left. Later the baby developed black stools, indicating that some lye had got into the stomach and was causing bleeding somewhere high in the intestinal track. But he did recover.

That nightmarish night is still vivid in Reverend Fraser's mind. He told me recently his recollection of the incident: "The night Lloyd swallowed the lye, I was having supper down at Alex

Morrison's at Wreck Cove. The telegraph office was right there in Alex's house. I knew a telegram came in from North River and I knew something was wrong, but I was not told until after I finished eating what the problem was. I had a good horse and I drove home as fast as I could. The poor boy was in bad shape, gasping for breath.

"When I saw Lloyd my thoughts were that, whatever was going to happen, God was with us. God would sustain us. They told me Dannie Morrison had gone to meet the doctor at South Gut, and I was glad to know the doctor was on the way. We felt the time long enough but there was a sense of God's upholding, giving grace and courage. We had so much faith in the doctor that I knew when he came he would do something to relieve the terrible strain. The baby was so short of breath.

"Our good friends and neighbors were praying for us. Sarah MacDonald, Christie Effie's aunt, was praying all night. Whatever the doctor did, the baby began to get better, and by daylight I think he was really promising. Dr. MacMillan was the one God used to save our boy."

Reverend Fraser reminded me of another emergency when I had to be called in. He himself had a very severe attack of asthma. When I arrived he was in pretty bad shape. As he recalls it, my first question was, "How are you?" and he answered, "I'm pretty near gone." And then, he tells me, my comment was, "You've lost your faith."

I'll let Archie carry on with the story: "The doctor prepared a needle and gave it to me. After a while my breath came, and the asthma cleared right up. I felt all right. The doctor looked at me and asked, 'Have you got your faith back now?' "

One day in the winter of 1934 I was out with "Freddie Bank"—that is, Freddie MacDonald who worked in the Royal Bank of Canada in Baddeck. We were cruising up and down the ice about a mile from the south side of the lake, probably a couple of miles east of the line of bushes, when Freddie said to me, "Doc, I've got an awful pain in my stomach."

My first thought was that it might be something serious, and I wondered whether I should drive him right over to the railway station. He would have to wait there a few hours for the evening train to Sydney Mines, which was his home. If his pain meant something serious, he would be handy to the hospital.

While I was considering the matter, he said, "Well, maybe it's just my dinner. I had a big dinner with roast pork, gravy, potatoes, and carrots." In a short time his pain eased up somewhat, and we concluded he had merely had a case of indigestion. I decided we would head for Baddeck, and then if the pain grew bad again, or I found some indication that there was serious trouble, I'd still have time to get him across the lake to catch the evening train.

I drove toward the bushes that marked the way to Baddeck, but before I reached the bush line, a sudden storm came up. It was snowing and blowing so hard that it was only with luck we found our way home. We would never have found our way if we hadn't picked up the bushes just as the storm hit. Freddie kept his head out of the window all the way over to help locate the bushes. I was having trouble keeping the snow off the windshield with the windshield wiper. He seemed to be feeling better and didn't mention the pain again.

When we got to Baddeck I went about my duties and he got out of the car and went elsewhere. I guess we both just dismissed the incident from our minds. But an hour later the pain returned. He went to my house and asked Jessie to find me, at once wherever I was. As usual, she located me quickly. When I saw him in the office, I was sufficiently concerned about his condition to insist that he go to bed in my house, instead of returning to his room in the hotel. I put him in a bed upstairs and gave him a hypo of morphine. By this time I was pretty sure he had a perforated ulcer. He needed to go to the hospital, but by now the storm was so fierce there was no God's way in the world of getting him there. I wished mightily that I had followed my first thought that afternoon and had taken him to the train. If I had, he would be safe in the hospital by this time.

Jessie remembers well that night Freddie spent at our house: "You put Freddie to bed and told me you might not be home all night as you were going out on a confinement case. You said I shouldn't give him even a glass of water. I've forgotten now where you were going. After a while Freddie was asleep and I went to bed. Then I woke up and heard him moaning. He moaned for about two hours and I thought it was the beginning of the end for him. Finally he quieted down. When I couldn't hear any more moaning, I thought he had died and after that I couldn't sleep any more. I didn't sleep until you came home. You got in about five in the morning. I heard you come in and go upstairs, and then I heard you talking to Freddie, so I knew he was still alive.

"When I got up in the morning, I gave you and the children breakfast, and then I went up to see Freddie. I told him what a fright he had given me with his moaning, and that I thought he had died. He said, 'If I had known I was moaning, I wouldn't have. I remember when my mother was dying, she moaned half the night. I never want to hear anyone moan again.' "

When morning came, it was still too stormy. There was still no way to get him to the hospital for the operation he had to have. Finally, later in the day the storm lifted a little and we set out. We had Freddie in a sleigh with a lot of straw, hot-water bottles, and blankets to keep him warm. The temperature was below zero. We had to build bridges over the cracks on the ice in order to get across with horse and sleigh. We got to Shenacadie in time to catch the eight o'clock train that evening. Freddie's father met us with an ambulance at the station in Sydney Mines, and we reached the hospital about 10:30.

Freddie's family doctor, a surgeon, was there to meet us and we went right to the operating room. This was now more than twenty-four hours after his perforation. It probably began first as a little pinpoint perforation, which plugged so he seemed better for a time. Eventually the opening in the stomach got much bigger. When the surgeon opened Freddie's abdomen, he found it full of stomach contents, with pieces of carrot floating around. The ulcer was difficult to locate. Three times before the surgeon found the perforation, Freddie seemed to go into collapse, stopped breathing, and had to have artificial respiration. Whether he had any cardiac arrest, I don't know, but I know the anesthetists gave him some pretty good whacks on the chest. After the third episode the surgeon said, "Boys, I think we'd better close him up and send him to the ward."

I said, "Doctor, he might as well die on the table as die in the ward tomorrow." I couldn't see how he could survive. We had even sucked stomach contents out from around the liver and down in the pelvis with a suction machine. I couldn't see anything but peritonitis and death in a few days if we sent him back to the ward. I think, judging from the expression on his face, that the surgeon was greatly relieved when I said that. "All right," he said, "you brought him in. He's your patient. We'll carry on."

Eventually the surgeon got to the back wall of the stomach, found the perforation, and sutured it. Freddie was back at work in the bank within five weeks of his operation.

At exactly seven o'clock in the morning of November 16, 1935, the telephone by my bedside rang. Mrs. Malcolm Dan MacNeil of Grass Cove wanted me to come over on the morning mail boat. She said Mary, her nine-year-old daughter, had taken a pain during the night, and even though the mother realized it must be something more than a plain stomach ache, she had waited until morning to call. She wanted me to catch the 7:30 boat, which would make a much shorter trip than the thirty-eight miles by road.

Unfortunately, she was mistaken about the time the boat left in the morning. While she was talking, I raised my head, looked out the window, and saw that the boat was already untied and backing out from the wharf. I said, "Hang up quick! The boat's leaving now." Then I called Central and asked her to call the wharf, get the wharfinger, Willie MacRitchie, to hail the boat and get them back. Then I dressed in a hurry. I was down to the wharf in less than five minutes, jumped aboard the boat just as she pulled in, hung onto the rail as the captain swung the wheel, and I was on my way to Iona.

Someone met me at Iona and drove me the two miles to the MacNeil home. There was no question about the diagnosis. Mary had a red-hot appendix. She had to get to the hospital fast. Her father, Malcolm Dan, was working at the gypsum quarry at Little Narrows. It would take at least two hours to get a message to him and get him home, and that might be just two hours too much. One of the neighbors, Jimmy J. D., drove us to the North Sydney hospital.

The operating room was all set up and Dr. Meech and his assistant were waiting. As usual, I assisted Dr. Meech while his assistant gave the anesthetic. The appendix was gangrenous—careful handling was called for, as there were several pinpoint holes beginning to ooze. A drain was inserted before the abdomen was closed.

Mary came back home on December 6, in very good condition. I'm glad her appendix kicked up before winter set in, while the boat was still operating and the roads were open.

Any time you have to deal with gangrene, you have an emergency. I remember when I was taking care of Big John MacRae of Baddeck. He was a man in his late seventies and had been a widower for many years. With him lived his nephew and wife, Mr. and Mrs. Hector MacRae, and their family. They looked after Big John and gave him the best of care.

When he called me in to see him, Big John was complaining of pain in his leg. Soon there was redness and swelling. Then the leg began to get cold and black. Diagnosis: gangrene.

Big John was sent to the North Sydney Hospital for amputation. The night before his operation, probably as a result of the narcotic given him, he wet the bed. This he didn't like, so he got out of his own bed, put the person next to him in the ward out of his bed, and crawled in.

Soon he wet the second bed, so he moved to a third, again dispossessing another patient. I don't know how many beds he had wet before the nurse came in and found a hullabaloo in the ward. It became a question of whether to keep Big John in the hospital or send him home and keep the rest of the patients in the ward.

So early the next morning, I got a call from the hospital to take Big John out of there. Hector and I drove down to bring him home, and once there, he was perfectly sane. But here we were in a small village, a man with gangrene in his leg, no hospital, and what were we going to do? We realized Big John just couldn't endure being away from home in a strange place.

Sadie, Hector's wife, had been through a similar experience once before. Her grandfather, known as Big Angus MacDonald, had had gangrene in his leg. He had absolutely refused to have his leg removed or to go into any hospital. He lived with that gangrenous leg for three or four months. The leg got so rotten it was almost impossible to live in the house with him. Though the family gave him the best of care, it was a hard experience for them. They felt that even though he was a man over eighty years of age, if he was able to endure gangrene of the leg for three or four months and still live, his constitution would have been strong enough to withstand amputation of the leg, and perhaps he would have lived for years. As a result of that experience, Sadie knew what to expect. But the question was what to do with Big John. With Sadie's and Hector's consent, I decided to remove the leg at home.

The pioneer doctors in this area had had no hospital anywhere to send anybody for a thing like this. It was a common occurrence for them to do amputations in the country homes. For many years, however, we had had hospitals in Cape Breton Island, so to undertake this type of surgery in the home was a major event.

I asked Dr. M. G. MacLeod of Whycocomagh to come to Baddeck to assist me. The local public health nurse, Miss Phyllis Lyttle, and Mrs. Margaret MacCharles, an R.N., completed the team. Mrs. MacCharles did most of the work of sterilization and preparing for the operation. I interviewed her to obtain her recollection of the case.

"I remember the doctor approaching me when he decided to operate. It was on April 5, 1946, that we removed the leg. Miss Lyttle and I prepared everything. We did most of the sterilization with a pressure cooker, that is, the drapes, towels, Dr. MacMillan's gown and gloves. The instruments were all sterilized on the kitchen stove. The hunting knife and saw he used were sharpened at

MacFarlane's Garage and then soaked in an antiseptic solution for some hours.

"If I remember correctly, I think we were there all morning getting things ready. The operating table was made by Malcolm MacRae of West Middle River, who at that time was working at Pinaud's Yacht Yard. The table was set up in Mr. MacRae's bedroom, to take advantage of the window light. This room was as sterile as any operating room when we started the operation in early afternoon.

"Dr. MacMillan operated under a spinal anesthetic, and while this was taking effect, he scrubbed up. He and Miss Lyttle both scrubbed. Dr. MacLeod was there as moral support. He had a terrific bedside manner and kept Mr. MacRae very cheerful and comfortable. At different times during the operation he had to administer some medication by needle when the pressure got too low.

"I remember mostly having to steady the leg. I did not scrub, but I took a sterile towel to steady the leg further up as Dr. MacMillan was amputating. After it was off, Dr. MacMillan walked out carrying the leg, and then later on, when we were all through, he took it home and burned it in his furnace. He said it reminded him of the story of 'The Cremation of Sam MacGee.'"

Big John got along very well following the operation. He lived until the leg completely healed. Unfortunately, about this time, he developed prostate trouble, and also an infection from the frequent use of a catheter. I had hoped to be able to handle the prostate trouble to get him well enough or strong enough to do something about it. But when deterioration set in, it was very rapid. John passed away a little over six weeks after the amputation.

I thought back to the afternoon I first arrived in Baddeck to establish practice. I checked in at the hotel, looked at the place I was to use as an office, unloaded my car of the meager amount of supplies I had, and then decided to go for a swim. I went down to the wharf and had just got into the water when Willie Mac-Ritchie, the wharfinger, came and called me. He said, "You're on duty. There's a patient here to see you." That first patient was Big John MacRae.

In 1954, *Maclean's* magazine carried an article about some unusual incidents in my practice, and one of the stories concerned my use of a speedometer cable housing to dislodge a piece of meat stuck in a patient's gullet.

I was down at North River one day in August of 1946 when I received word by telephone that I was needed immediately at Red Jim MacNeil's at Jamesville, near Iona. Red Jim had a piece of meat stuck in his gullet and was having great difficulty getting his breath.

I finished my work at North River as quickly as possible and started for Jamesville. Passing through Baddeck, I stopped at Norman Bethune's Garage. I said to Norman, "I want something very flexible and very smooth at the end." Immediately Norman reached up to some pegs above him and picked out a speedometer cable housing. It looked to be of just the right size for an esophageal bougie, so I told him that was fine. He took it to the emery wheel and polished it very, very smooth, gave it to me, and away I went.

When I got to Little Narrows Ferry I met Dr. Mickey R. MacDonald and Dr. Albert Fownes returning from Jamesville. They were vacationing at the Inverary Inn and had been pressured into going to see Red Jim since it was uncertain how long it would take me to finish up at North River and get there. They had tried to push the meat through to the stomach using a length of rubber tubing from a stethoscope. This didn't work, so they ordered him to the hospital in North Sydney. They were confident he would make the hospital all right.

I almost turned back to Baddeck, but then decided to go see the family anyway. When I got to the MacNeil home, Red Jim was still there. Not a word was mentioned about the two doctors who had been to see him or about the fact that they had ordered him to go to the hospital. I watched him for a while. If he swallowed two or three times, he would get relief for a few minutes. It was very evident that he expected me to do something.

I put Red Jim on the kitchen table, got his head bent well backward and told him to swallow. Just as he swallowed, I introduced the smoothed-down cable housing into the esophagus. Within one minute the makeshift esophageal bougie was down to the stomach, and that was it. He got complete relief right away. Red Jim was sixty-four years old at that time; he died in the fall of 1968 at the age of eighty-six.

As the years went by, this story got considerable publicity. It became greatly exaggerated. Someone even said I was seen that day driving toward Jamesville and the car seemed to be going by itself. I couldn't be seen at all. The implication was that I was bending over the floorboards of the car and tearing out the speedometer cable housing, getting ready to do the job.

That speedometer cable housing hung in my office for a few years and in that time I used it three or four times. Then I decided I had better do better than that and I bought a mercury-loaded esophageal bougie. I used that a few times, too, and perhaps it looked more professional, but it didn't do a bit better job than the one Norman Bethune provided.

When a doctor carries on a general practice in the country, there come times when he would give most anything to have the medical facilities of a modern hospital somehow packed into his bag. One such time came when I was called to Dan R. MacNeil's home at Red Point, about thirty-three miles from Baddeck. Mrs. MacNeil had severe pain, and my tentative diagnosis was kidney colic.

I had my microscope with me and I asked her for a specimen so I could find out if there were any blood cells in the urine. This would clinch the diagnosis of a stone in the kidney. She said she was in too much pain to give me a specimen. She was in agony. I told her I would give her a sedative, let her rest a few minutes while it took effect, and then we'd get a specimen. I reached into my bag and pulled out a 30 c.c. vial of a drug I had been using for a few years. I gave her 2 c.c. intramuscularly.

Those were the days when I was working hard and every minute I had a chance to do so, I would lie down and rest. I went out of the patient's room and lay down on the couch in the kitchen prepared for ten minutes sleep. I was just beginning to relax when Dan R. called, "Doctor, come in!" I went in, and his wife looked like death. She was not breathing. There were no heart sounds. She was dead.

Now it just happened that I had spent the previous evening with Dr. Jarmen at Red Head. He had explained to me that the newest method of treating cardiac arrest was external cardiac massage. Before this time the standard method of treatment was opening up the chest wall and massaging the heart. He had explained to me how the new procedure of external cardiac massage was done. I didn't dream I would be using the new technique so soon.

Putting the heels of both hands over the chest, I put all my weight into pressure on the heart several times; then, without taking time to listen for heart sounds with the stethoscope, I started artificial respiration. It was just seven minutes before I could feel her assisting me. In twenty minutes she was conscious and breathing on her own.

While I was doing the resuscitation her husband contacted the priest on the telephone. Those few minutes seemed like a lifetime to me. By the time the priest arrived the patient was all right, but I was limp, thinking of the near catastrophe.

I took Mrs. MacNeil back to the hospital with me and ran two quarts of fluid through her veins and got the stone that night. It was a tough way to get a kidney stone.

In discussing this experience with me, Mrs. MacNeil said she could remember my coming to the house when she had the kidney colic and she could remember my giving her the needle. The journey to Baddeck was like a dream to her. Her first clear memory was of getting intravenous treatment at the hospital.

One very frequent type of emergency was the old man with prostate enlargement and urinary retention. Most of these patients could be relieved with a catheter and so were not an emergency but just a routine procedure. Even when a catheter could not be passed, if the roads were open to North Sydney the case was not really an emergency. But in the winter time, when a catheter could not be passed, when the roads were not open for travel and transportation to a hospital would take hours—then I had an emergency.

Jimmie MacKenzie of Washabuck reminded me of one such case: "One night I was out to my neighbor's place, Rory MacLean, who lived on the mountain. He had a terrible pain in his bladder. The old gent was getting no better and by one o'clock in the morning he was in agony. I told his family to send for the doctor and I would go after him. I went home, harnessed my horse to the sleigh, and headed for the ice. There was two and a half feet of snow with a bad crust, which made traveling slow. I saw a light coming out of the harbor around the western end of Kidston's Island. I made for it and met the doctor walking and carrying his bags and a lantern. When we reached the shore on the way back, the horse's legs above the knees were chafed and bleeding from breaking through the crust."

When I reached Old Rory, I found that he had not passed water for very nearly forty-eight hours; the bladder could be felt quite prominently up as far as the navel. I used all the catheters I had, but could not give him any relief. The only thing to do then was to do a suprapubic under local anesthesia, involving an incision in the lower part of the abdomen. You can't make many mistakes in a case like that, because the bladder is so distended that it's pushed the peritoneum out of the way. I carried my scalpel down until I got to the bladder well, picked up the bladder wall with a pair of artery forceps and make a nick in the bladder. Then I inserted a catheter tube and left it in. It was a great relief to the patient; he could now be moved in comfort to the hospital when weather and traveling conditions on the ice were good.

Another neighbor of Old Rory, Alex D. MacLean of Washabuck Bridge, added a little to the story of that night: "Doctor, your memory is pretty good, but you're overlooking one thing. You were practically exhausted that night when you came to attend that gentleman at Washabuck. You got over here and relieved his pain and did the best you could for him. Then you turned around to his wife and asked if she had a telephone. 'No,' she said, 'we have no telephone.' 'Well,' you said, 'that's good. Show me a bed.' "

THE STORK IN TROUBLE

The anxieties and fears I had occasionally in the years I was doing home deliveries were soon forgotten if the result was "mother and baby are doing fine." There were a few times when this could not be said, and these are the stories I remember.

The first winter I was here, Ernest Carmichael of Baddeck Forks was seriously ill. He was not a strong or robust man at best, and now he had lobar pneumonia in both lungs. His wife, who was taking care of him, was in her eighth month of pregnancy. I had been to see Ernest several times and I had little hope that he would recover. When I went out to see him on a Sunday morning, she was sick, too, but she didn't tell me. She felt she had to carry on, because he needed her care. However, at four that afternoon she was so sick that she couldn't stay on her feet any longer and lay down on a couch in the living room. When some of the neighbors stopped in and saw how she was, they phoned me. I wasn't at home but the telephone operator found me not too far away and I started right out, reaching Baddeck Forks by horse and sleigh at seven that evening. I found Mrs. Carmichael had a temperature of 105 degrees, pulse of 140, and she showed definite signs of starting labor. It was a serious situation and I was frightened. But how frightened can you get? I had the answer to that question before the night was over.

I called the neighborhood midwife, Mrs. Mackenzie, on the telephone and found that she was in church. Giving Mrs. Carmichael instructions not to move from the couch, I set off for the church in my sleigh. Mrs. Mackenzie, the midwife, left in the middle of the service and we hurried back. There was no question that Mrs. Carmichael was going to have her baby that night. With the help of neighbors, we got her to her own bedroom upstairs.

About midnight she had complete dilatation of the cervix. She was ready to deliver. In order to shorten her labor as much as I could, I decided to use instruments. By this time she wasn't strong enough to put any force into her contractions to help the birth.

Mrs. MacKenzie administered a good anesthetic for me while I was scrubbing up, then held the kerosene lamp while I got the instruments on. The lamp was a large one that held more than a pint of kerosene. Just as I applied the instruments, Mrs. MacKenzie dropped the lamp! The odd thing was, the shade didn't break, but the lamp itself broke and the kerosene spilled. Instantly, there was a fire from the floor right up to the ceiling of the room. Fortunately, and perhaps the Lord was with us, the lamp had fallen on a large mat. I dropped what I was doing and within a very few seconds rolled up the mat, blaze and all. Somebody opened the window for me and we threw the mat out the window without anyone being burned. Then, while the room was still dark, except for some light from the blaze outside, I delivered the baby. We did get another lamp in the room by the time it was necessary to attend to the mother and child.

The baby was very limp, with a slow heart-beat but no breathing, until I spent several minutes with mouth-to-mouth resuscitation. But due perhaps to the mother's condition and the fact that she had flu, and also because the baby was premature, the child didn't gain any strength. When I left I asked the nurse to give the baby a little slap on the bottom once in a while to see if she could get it to cry. But the baby just wasn't strong enough to cough or get any mucus out of the chest. It died the next day about noon. When I called again the following day, I discovered Mrs. Carmichael had pneumonia. Ernest, her husband, passed away a few days later on January 18. Mrs. Carmichael survived. She has since remarried and has a fine family.

There were a few occasions when I had to send to the nearest medical center for help in a difficult delivery. That happened on December 20, 1930, when I was called to Englishtown. It was very stormy and my car got stuck in the snow on Rockyside. Someone on the other end had anticipated this, and before I had walked very far I was met by someone with a horse and sleigh.

I found the patient in very heavy labor. In a few hours it became very obvious that she would never deliver the baby herself. Furthermore, after a trial with anesthesia and forceps, it was obvious that I could not deliver the baby. So I called Dr. Meech of North Sydney and asked him to come to Englishtown. Because of the snow, he had to take the long way around, via Ross Ferry.

I administered the anesthesia again and after another unsuccessful attempt with instruments, Dr. Meech finally delivered the child by internal version, that is, by turning the baby end for end and delivering it feet first. The baby was stillborn, but the mother's future pregnancies and deliveries were normal.

The second time I had to send for help was on December 1, 1931. The problem was an arm presentation, the baby in transverse position. I called in Dr. Frank MacLeod from Inverness. Dr. Frank did the internal version and I administered the anesthesia. The success of doing an internal versions depends a great deal on the anesthetic.

It was very fortunate that there were two doctors present. I looked after the baby and Dr. Frank looked after the mother. I think I had the most worry because I had to use artificial respiration for a long time. I didn't time how long I was using mouth-to-mouth breathing, but I remember thinking during the last several minutes that it was hopeless. But I persisted, and I was finally rewarded when Anna MacRae of Middle River, Victoria County, came to life.

Sometimes problem confinements seemed to come in batches. One such sequence started early in the morning of January 20, 1934. The first call came from John Philip Morrison who, with his wife Christine, was living with her family in Upper Baddeck River, about thirteen or more miles out from town. John remembers that morning: "I got up early and decided to go fishing at North Gut. For some reason I went back upstairs after breakfast, and I found Christine unconscious, her eyes rolled back, and frothing at the mouth. I got a horse ready and had to drive down about six miles to the nearest telephone to call you. The weather was quite stormy."

When I got the call, the party on the other end of the line was so excited that I couldn't make out what kind of a case it was. He said she was "bleeding" from the mouth and I couldn't get any more out of him than that. I got ready as fast as I could, putting my pneumothorax machine in the sleigh because, from what I could gather, I thought she might be having a pulmonary hemorrhage.

It was mid-afternoon before I arrived at the home and found that Christine was six months pregnant and having convulsions. She had had many convulsions between the time they phoned me in the morning and the time I arrived. She had several more after I arrived, but I finally got them under control.

Although Mrs. Morrison was completely unconscious, she was having a few contractions, and during the night she definitely went into labor. Looking for moral support, I asked John Phillip to go again to the telephone and call Dr. Gillis and ask him to come out. I planned, when the labor was far enough advanced and there was dilatation of the cervix, to put on instruments and deliver her as soon as I could. If I remember correctly, Dr. Gillis made the trip in about three hours. By this time there had been some horses on the road, so the going wasn't as heavy as when I came out.

I suppose Dr. Gillis was there about two hours before I deemed Mrs. Morrison ready for delivery. I knew the baby was already dead. I had examined the patient very carefully and I could find no fetal heartbeat whatever. Dr. Gillis gave her some anesthetic, even though she was unconscious, and I put instruments on and delivered her.

It was some time the next morning before Mrs. Morrison's condition improved to a state where we could leave her. She did not regain consciousness for three days, but after that she was all right.

I learned later that during that same night, while both Dr. Gillis and I were busy with Mrs. John Philip Morrison in Upper Baddeck River, six miles from a telephone, Mrs. J. K. Morrison of Red Head went into labor. Mrs. Margaret MacCharles, a trained nurse, delivered the child. It was a normal delivery except that the infant was born with a caul, that is, the membrane was still over the face. If there hadn't been someone there who was aware enough to remove it, the baby would not have survived. It was only a matter of wiping off the membrane and then giving the usual attention to a newborn baby who has mucus in the throat or chest. The baby born that night was Murdoch Morrison.

Meanwhile, back in Upper Baddeck, we were just ready to leave for home when a message came from Ingonish. I was needed there to see to a woman who had been in labor for three days and nights, off and on. I thought hard about how much snow had fallen during the previous few days, And I thought about that long drive over Smoky to Ingonish. I was sure I couldn't get there by horse and sleigh in less than three days and nights.

I stopped in at the farm in Big Baddeck where there was a telephone, called the Cape Breton Flying Club, and made arrangements to have a plane on the ice in front of the Baddeck Yacht Club about the same time I could get there. (I'll tell about that plane trip in another chapter—it was really one for the books.)

When I arrived at the patient's home in Ingonish, I found Mrs. Baker, a very good nurse, taking care of things. She remembered the case well: "I was there four or five days, came home and made trips back and forth, and sometimes stayed overnight. The patient was in very hard labor for one whole night. The telegraph office then was at the ferry, and I sent for Dr. MacMillan to come as soon as possible. She was kind of a difficult patient to handle because you couldn't depend on what she'd tell you about the pains. Anyway, it was within the hour after the doctor arrived that the twins were born."

The first baby came normally, but the second was in a transverse position. The arm presented itself first. I had to do an internal version under general anesthesia. This was the first internal version I had done by myself, but there was no question of getting another doctor to Ingonish to help that night. Mrs. Baker administered the chloroform for me, and pretty soon we had the second baby. The experience I gained that night stood me in good stead at future deliveries.

Mrs. Baker remembered taking care of the babies for a few days. "They were premature, so we oiled them and wrapped them in cotton wool, and fed them by dropper. I fixed little beds for them in boxes, one a Borden's milk box and the other a Carnation milk box.

We were sitting by, watching the babies, and one of them made a little cry. I asked the neighbor lady who was with me which of the babies was crying. She looked down and said, 'Carnation.' So after that they were called 'Borden' and 'Carnation.' "

Mrs. Baker served that community well for many years. While making these notes I drove to Ingonish and talked with her (now Mrs. Whitty) about her experiences. I remarked that over the years she must have given a lot of service to the area and that she must have received a lot of pleasure and satisfaction out of that. She said she did indeed, "But no money!" She laughed at her own remark and added, "I'd get a bag of potatoes sometimes, or a codfish, but still I enjoyed it." She went wherever she was needed, sometimes staying two or three days, or even a week or two. "I'd get what they could give me, two dollars, four dollars, five dollars, but not always. I didn't expect it if they didn't have it."

Just to prove that not all obstetrical complications occur during blizzards, I'll tell about one case in the West Tarbot area in the summertime, when the traveling was fairly good. There was a patient there who was eight months pregnant and who had been hemorrhaging some time before she called me. By the time I got there, the bleeding had stopped and I just wondered what was going on.

I always remembered the instructions given by Dr. Atlee and the other professors at Medical School that a pregnant woman who was bleeding should never be examined unless the doctor was prepared to go ahead immediately with surgery. It was a rule I broke a few times. On those occasions I found that it wasn't as bad as it could have been and I was able to handle the cases at home. But this was one of the times I should have heeded what I had been taught.

I made the examination and found that the delivery was not imminent at all. I went downstairs then to think about what I would do. Then I heard her cry out, so I went right back up. She had started to hemorrhage again and hemorrhaged so profusely that she had become frightened, had jumped up, and had starting running. There was blood all over the room. I put her back to bed and the hemorrhage stopped. We got her padded up and, with assistance, put her in a blanket and carried her out to the back seat of my car. I was heading as fast as I could for North Sydney Hospital as I had decided the only chance there was for this woman was to have a Caesarian right away.

As I said, it was summertime, and I knew I could get her to the hospital within an hour. I had only gone a mile, or a mile and a half, when I looked back and there was blood running on the floor of the car and out the door. I figured then she wouldn't make it to North Sydney, so I turned in at the first gate, which happened to be Malcolm MacDonald's. I knew his daughter, Dolly, was home on vacation and she was a trained nurse.

Immediately, we cleared the kitchen, put the patient on the kitchen table. By this time she had some dilatation of the neck of the womb and I gave her a little pitocin. We delivered the baby in fairly short order, but the baby had not survived; in fact, it had probably died with the first hemorrhage.

Another hurried trip to the North Sydney hospital came in mid-March, 1938. Mrs. Malcolm MacLean came to my office on Saturday evening for a routine pre-natal examination. As far as I can remember now, she had had no previous symptoms of trouble at all. When I examined her I found one-plus albumin in the urine and a slight rise in blood pressure. I wasn't alarmed. She only had a month to go and I was quite sure that, with rest and proper diet, we could carry her through to term.

That night, however, after arriving home, around ten or eleven o'clock she had considerable abdominal distress. She attributed this distress to the usual Saturday night supper of baked beans. The discomfort was relieved by a dose of baking soda and she quieted down and finally fell asleep.

The next morning, Sunday, March 13, she went into convulsions, and I received a rush call to Big Baddeck. At the time Mrs. MacLean was living on what we call "the Big Farm Road," about five or six miles from Baddeck. I had to take the horse and sleigh and Jimmie MacIvor went with me. When I arrived at their home, I found Margaret unconscious. The question was how to move her from her home to the Hamilton Hospital in North Sydney over snowbound roads.

We telephoned ahead and found that the road was open for a car from North Sydney up Boulardarie Island to Kempt Head, which is at the western end of Boulardarie, southeast across the lake from Baddeck.

I gave Margaret some anti-convulsive treatment by needle. Then we made a bed for her in a box sleigh, put a pile of blankets and some hot-water bottles around her, and started out with Duncan Buchanan driving the horse. Duncan and I had a seat over the front end and Margaret was lying down in the sleigh.

When we arrived at Kempt Head, we made the main highway and found the car waiting for us. While we were transferring Margaret from the box sleigh to the car, she regained consciousness. I would judge the amount of blankets we covered her with had brought her out in a heavy perspiration and probably had something to do with her recovery up to that point. I knew she would be in the hospital in a very short time, so I turned back for home.

When she got into the hospital she was considerably improved, but the following Wednesday she went into convulsions again.

On Thursday morning, the 17th, she had a Caesarian section done and the result was a live baby, a boy, Neil Allen.

Marguerite Morrison of Englishtown was a vital link in my "telephone answering service." She operated the Central at Englishtown, and any time I was in her district, she could always pinpoint me within a very few minutes if she had to relay a message that I was needed elsewhere. For thirty-seven years she kept track of my comings and goings. "It wasn't too easy at times," she told me, "but if an emergency arose, I would find where you were and get you to the nearest telephone. In those days there weren't too many telephones and perhaps you would be some distance from one, but I would call the nearest neighbor and they would go out and get you and bring you to a telephone."

Marguerite called me about six in the morning of January 15, 1948. She said, "Doctor, I thought I'd let you know you'd better stick around home today because I might need you." I said, "Marguerite, remember you had a baby last year and you weren't too long in labor, so we'd better come right now."

I put the coffee pot on the stove, called the nurse, and we had a cup of coffee together before starting out. At the time it didn't seem there was any rush. The call came at six o'clock, and by seven we were in Englishtown, eighteen miles away. As soon as we reached Marguerite's home we were told the baby had already arrived and everything was all right. We went upstairs and found Marguerite in bed. There were several women sitting around but no sign of the baby. I asked, "Where's the baby?" She said, "It's in the bed." Nobody had lifted the blankets to look at the baby or give it any attention!

The baby was dead, as dead as it would ever be. I couldn't say how long it had been dead, but the women said it had arrived about 25 minutes before we got there. The women also told us that as soon as it was born, they had heard one little gasp, then they heard no more. The baby must have been supplied with mother's blood for a considerable time after it was born. But when I examined it, there was no heartbeat, no breathing, and the infant was white.

The medical teaching is that for every minute a newborn baby goes without circulation after birth there is more brain damage. Fortunately that morning I had a needle and syringe already sterilized in my bag. I clamped the cord and I gave the baby 2 c.c. of coramine in the umbilical vein. There was immediate muscular spasm. I was sure the heart started to beat then. Then we started mouth-to-mouth breathing, which we kept up for forty-five minutes. We'd have to stop a few seconds now and then to aspirate mucus, which was coming out of the chest from the mouth-to-mouth breathing. We took turns.

I'm afraid the mother got very little attention, but it meant just as much to the mother as to myself to attend to the baby first. It was after the breathing was well established and the baby lad a good color that I looked after the mother.

The baby was a girl and was named Mary, and I've watched her career very carefully and with interest. Now she is grown and holding down a good position. This is a story I'm glad to record. Some I remember only because something went wrong, but this one I recall vividly because something very wrong turned out very well.

In December 1941 I had a call to see Mrs. George Barron Ingonish Harbour. She was about seven months pregnant and hemorrhaging. As usual, the trip over Smoky proved difficult. I started out in my car and the going was good until I reached North Shore, and buried my car in a snowdrift at Wreck Cove. I walked on to Sandy MacDermid's and enquired there about getting someone to drive me in a horse and sleigh. I was told Donnie Morrison had the best driver in the district. He agreed to take me.

Donnie says this about the trip to Ingonish: "We left home about five o'clock. There was quite a bit of snow and I walked all the way up Smoky. Dr. MacMillan walked part way. Down at Ingonish, the road was after drifting in and we got into a snowbank we hadn't expected. The sleigh capsized and we spilled out. I managed to hold onto the reins. We got to Ingonish Harbour about seven-thirty or eight o'clock at night, and were there until four o'clock in the morning."

I found Mrs. Barron in poor condition. She had hemorrhaged badly and was just about bled out. Her color was like pure white paper. But the bleeding had stopped before I got there.

I was in quite a predicament then. There was no God's way in the world to get her to a hospital. You certainly couldn't take a woman in that condition over Smoky by horse and sleigh, and then fifty or sixty miles more by car to a hospital. I learned that the coastal vessel, ASPY, might be in Ingonish in two or three days, but at the time there was ice and no assurance that the vessel would be able to get there in three days on her regular trip. And I couldn't stay and look after her while waiting for the boat. I had more than five thousand people in my own end of the county to look after.

I had no blood with me, no plasma, and no way of getting any. Although she had lost a lot of blood and was very white, she seemed quite strong. So I did the only thing I could under the circumstances. I administered about 2/10 c.c. of pitocin to induce labor. Surprisingly, within fifteen or twenty minutes, labor began. After about two or three hours of labor, the baby was born, dead as expected. This time, too, I had the comfort and assistance of Mrs. Baker's services.

After the delivery, the patient seemed no worse for the experience, and she lived to have three or four more healthy children. It was one of those cases where everything turned out all right for the patient, but had I lost the patient it would have been a different story.

I was making some calls in Englishtown on July 26, 1952, I received word that Mrs. Marie Urquhart, who was expecting within the next month or so, would like to see me. That day she had eaten some home-canned salmon and had become very sick with food poisoning. She was so sick that I became alarmed and took her back with me to the Baddeck Hospital. My great fear was that she might go into labor before she recovered from the food poisoning. And sure enough, she did. She started labor that night, and although she was not in too good condition when labor started, she improved as labor progressed. She delivered about 1:00 PM the next day, Sunday, and she and the baby appeared to be fine.

I had been at the hospital with her all night and by now was getting a little tired. At two I told the nurses I was going to pick up my family and take them to the beach, three miles west of Baddeck, for a swim. I had just changed into my swimming trunks when I saw a truck coming up the road, driving like mad, both doors open and flapping. The driver was Ada MacCharles, one of the nurses. She told me Marie was bleeding badly. Ada didn't know whose truck she had. It was sitting in front of hospital and she just took it.

Back in the maternity ward, I found Marie in shock and still bleeding. I put one hand on the abdominal wall and massaged the uterus while the nurses administered drugs intravenously and intramuscularly. Our attempts to contract the uterus and control bleeding were of no avail.

I never in all my experiences, either before or after this case, saw a woman lose so much blood. It was just like turning on the tap full force every few minutes. I finally had to put all my weight top of the uterus, squeeze it down into the pelvis and hold it there for two hours. It hurt, yes, but the patient was very cooperative, knowing that her very life depended on my being able to control the hemorrhage. She laughs now and says, "When I began to cry, Dr. MacMillan told me to swear instead. I did, and it seemed to help."

None of us can remember now how or when we first got blood up from the blood bank in North Sydney for Marie. While we were waiting for it to come, we used some blood plasma, a quart of a special intravenous fluid generally referred to as "artificial blood," and intravenous glucose and saline to combat dehydration. My notes on the chart say she received four pints of whole blood.

The patient had a very stormy time for a few days, and I got very little rest. Now, just about twenty years later, Marie looks very little older than she did then.

We never really knew what conditions we would have to work under on country calls. Ralph Pinaud remembered another time he took "a little drive" into the country with me. It was a call to a house in a very desolate area. Ralph waited in the car while I went in to see the patient, a confinement case. "He was in there a while," Ralph says, "when suddenly the light went out. Apparently there was only the one lamp in the house. The doctor came running out to me and said, 'Back up the car and shine the lights in through the window.' I did it and I guess that was all the illumination he needed, because after a while he came out and told me the baby had been born."

It is a sad fact of life that a doctor, no matter how hard he tries, can't win in every case. And the losses are hard.

About two o'clock in the morning of December 1, 1952, I was called to Grand Narrows to attend the wife of the railway station agent. Although it was early winter, there had been some frost and a thaw. The roads were not in good condition. When I arrived at the home, I found I had another case of abruptio placentae, with considerable bleeding. I wanted to put the patient in my car and get into North Sydney Hospital as quickly as possible. But I was told the road was impassable and I would be certain to get stuck, probably several times, on the way. Who knows now? I might have been able to get through if I had tried and the story might have had a happy ending. I remember the similar case I had had in Ingonish, when it had been impossible to get the patient to the hospital. And I remembered several other similar cases over the years, when it was impossible to move the patient. This case was much more favorable because she was already in labor and during previous confinements she had had no trouble. Her other babies had come after short, natural labors.

I knew I could get blood up from North Sydney on the morning train. I telephoned the hospital in Baddeck and arranged for them to send a taxi over with some blood plasma. I thought this would help until the whole blood came in the morning. The thought of getting hopelessly mired in a mudhole en route to North Sydney with this patient was too much for me.

About the time I was reaching this decision, a freight train went by. I could have put her on this train and gone along with her, but I didn't want to do that either, as I feared the baby would be born before we reached the hospital.

The baby was born in less than two hours. The mother hemorrhaged again following the birth, then went into a sleep and slipped away very peacefully and quietly before the blood plasma arrived from Baddeck.

I noticed at the time of the postpartum hemorrhage that there was no clotting, but I didn't understand. About three years later, in 1955, the medical profession made a break-through on this type of complication. There is a spontaneous loss of fibrin in the blood. Without fibrin there is no coagulation, and without coagulation you are in real trouble, especially in an isolated area. This condition is called afibrinogen anemia. The treatment indicated is fibrinogen, a product extracted from whole blood and given intravenously. Unfortunately, it wasn't available at that time when I needed it.

11

EXTENDED CARE

$\mathcal{M}$ost of my stories so far have dealt with "one-shot" cases, patients who needed my services to handle a specific instance of illness, accident, or childbirth. That is not to say that I didn't see these same patients for a variety of reasons over the period of years. Indeed, it is safe to say that most of the residents in Victoria County, and particularly those in the environs of Baddeck, required my services more than once.

But there were a few with chronic disabilities on whom I was in regular attendance. One serious chronic ailment was tuberculosis. During my early years of practice, we ran into a lot more tuberculosis than we do these days. During the first ten years I was in Baddeck I lost approximately thirteen young people with this disease. Some of these patients were in the sanitorium at the time of death; some had been in the sanitorium and had been released. Six people died in one small area, all traced to one contact.

It wasn't easy at that time to get people to go to the sanitorium. The treatment there was rest and fresh air, a good liberal diet, and pneumo treatment. In some cases ribs were removed to collapse the lung. Because of the number of deaths among those treated at the sanitorium, many families refused to let their young people go there. It was where the patient belonged, but if the family wouldn't consent, I had to treat the patients at home.

For this reason I acquired a pneumothorax machine soon after starting my practice. The "machine" consisted of two bottles connected by tubing, and with water in each. When you raised one bottle, the water flowing into the other forced air out. This air was passed by tube into the pleural space in the patient's chest. Enough air forced into the chest would collapse the lung and give it a rest.

Dr. Charlie Beckwith, the Public Health Officer in Sydney, gave me some instructions in the use of a pneumothorax machine and in controlling pulmonary hemorrhage. At first I used it just for controlling hemorrhage; that was often the first indication that someone might have something wrong. After using the machine for a while, I started using it for treatment of pulmonary tuberculosis.

One of the first patients I treated with my machine was Jessie Ann Morrison of Wreck Cove. She became ill in June of 1934. I had her rest at home for a few months, and then in October we x-rayed her chest. Pneumothorax treatment was indicated. She didn't want to go to the "san," so I said I would give her the treatments at home.

That was the winter I have always thought of as "the long winter." I can remember quite distinctly that by the first of January that year I had been using the horse and sleigh entirely for a period of six weeks. When I first started we gave her 200 c.c. of what we called "gas treatment," but which was really room air. This was injected in between the lining that covers the lung and the lining that covers the pleural cavity. In the beginning, I had to give her the treatment every two or three days and after a while, when I got enough collapse, it had to be repeated every two weeks.

Jessie was in bed at home and didn't realize what a hard winter it was. It was quite a strain for me to get down to Wreck Cove every two weeks that winter. I'd leave home about seven in the morning of the first day of these trips. I did well if I could get to her home by seven or eight or nine o'clock in the evening. I would give her the treatment and then start back. I would usually spend the night at the home of Mrs. Hannah (Alex) Matheson at North Shore, a home where I stopped so often when I needed rest, and then take another two days and nights making calls along the way as I headed back to Baddeck. Sometimes I would come home via Englishtown and sometimes by way of Tarbot and North River. I would probably make twenty or so calls on the way home.

When the second winter approached, I told her it would be impossible to carry on pneumothorax treatment at her home for another winter. To take three days out of every two weeks on this trip was just more than I could stand along with all the other work, which was gradually increasing. She would have to go to the "san," at least for the winter months.

She agreed and went to Kentville in November of 1935 and stayed until June of 1936. Then she was home for the summer and I gave her the regular treatments until November, when the weather began closing in, and she went back to the sanitorium for the winter.

Another patient I had in my care over a period of years was Neil H. Gillis. He had a very tough time with repeated cases of surgery. Neil says now: "I can recall three occasions when you really stole me from the cemetery. I was in pretty bad shape. Each time you took me to the hospital in North Sydney and did your best, and it worked."

His wife remembers more of the details of his illnesses: "That first time, in October 1949, my husband had been at a party at the school house the night before. It was put on by the Cooperative Society and they all had a very good time. They were there most of the night. The next morning Neil wasn't feeling too well and he felt like that most of the day. In the evening, at the time to go for the cows, he got up and said he would go. But I persuaded him that he had better stay in bed; when he started getting ready to go he noticed that he had a swelling in his stomach, so I was able to convince him to stay where he was. I had to go to a neighbor's house to call the doctor. His pains got very severe. Finally the doctor came in, late at night. He ordered Neil to the hospital."

I recognized that Neil's abdominal muscles were quiet rigid and that there was acute tenderness. I knew something had ruptured. While we were fixing a comfortable place in the back seat of my car for him, some of the neighbors whispered to me, "You know, doctor, he was at the party last night. He may have had a few drinks; that may be all that's wrong with him." But I knew he was in real trouble, whether he had had a few drinks the night before or not. I wanted to get him to the operating room just as fast as I could.

A couple of the Murphy boys went down to North Sydney with me. Mrs. Gillis had phoned from the neighbor's house to warn the hospital that I was on the way in with an emergency.

By the time we arrived, the O.R. was all set up and blood was ready for transfusions. Dr. Meech was the head surgeon; I assisted.

When we got the abdomen open, it was full of blood that was pouring out so fast it was difficult to find where it came from. The surgeon got some swabs up around the spleen area and found considerable congestion in the vessels there. It seemed as if the bleeding was coming from the spleen. The surgeon reached in and lifted out the spleen, ligated the splenic ligament and removed it. Neil still kept bleeding and we still kept pumping in blood. After a lot of swabbing and a lot of suction, we discovered that the blood was coming from down in the pelvis. The surgeon reached down in the pelvis and pulled up a hemorrhagic mass which was ligated and removed. This mass, an enormous hemorrhage type of growth, was in the omentum, the "apron" that covers or protects the intestines in the abdomen. The diagnosis given was post-operational made by the pathologist.

Neil recovered well and went home. But it was just about two months later that I received another rush call to see him. Mrs. Gillis remembered that the pain came on suddenly. "After dinner, Neil decided he'd go down to MacLean's store for tobacco and tea. When he came home, he complained of a severe pain in his stomach. He lay down on a cot in the kitchen, but the pain was becoming worse and worse all the time. There was a neighbor in and I sent him to call the doctor. Before the doctor came, Neil became so sick that we had to call the priest."

Once again the two Murphy boys and I drove him to the hospital. When we opened the abdomen this time we didn't know what to expect, having removed a bleeding tumor from him just two months before. But what he had this time, though serious enough, was an intestinal obstruction caused by bands of adhesions that so often follow abdominal surgery. We got to it just a few hours after the pain started. It wasn't necessary to do any resection of the bowel; we just removed the twists and cut the adhesions that were causing the obstruction.

The next episode occurred on February 2, 1953. The first two times we had been able to reach the hospital quickly, with no transportation problems. It wasn't that easy in February. First Mrs. Gillis had trouble locating me. Apparently I was out making calls somewhere and not available to a telephone. While they were waiting for me to call back, Neil got worse and was so sick

Mrs. Gillis phoned Dr. Goldie of Whycocomagh. He examined Neil and decided that since I had treated him on the previous occasions and knew his condition, they had better wait until they could get in touch with me. As soon as I was located I phoned them and told the family to bring him to Baddeck. It was a very stormy night, but the Murphy brothers brought him to my office.

I examined him right in the car, and sent him right down to North Sydney. I followed in my own car. Mrs. Gillis recalls that there was a problem when we reached Ross Ferry. "The captain didn't want to take them across because of the weather and heavy seas. Dr. MacMillan insisted that it was an emergency and got the captain to make the trip."

Neil remembers that there was a little delay in starting the surgery because the anesthetist was busy on the floor below in the delivery room. He says he remembers hearing me say, "Cut him here. Cut him here."

I checked through the hospital records to refresh my memory on that operation and found his chart, but the operation sheet was missing. Neil tells me that it was an intestinal obstruction again.

Neil's next major illness came in the summer of 1955. Mrs. Gillis described the onset: "The morning of July 25, 1955, Neil wasn't feeling too well, but he went over to put some hay in. Our two little boys were with him. While trying to pitch hay up on the truck, he suddenly dropped with the load on the fork. The little boys were frightened. One of them ran up to get Hughie Gillis, a neighbor. Hughie came down and found him semiconscious. He sent one of the little boys for the priest. By this time the priest had rushed up from Iona, and he was completely unconscious. The neighbors all gathered. The doctor said he'd be over immediately, but in the meantime, everyone was afraid to move him. After the priest came, they put him on the truck and brought him to the house. Then the doctor arrived and, after giving him some medicine, took him in the car to Baddeck."

This time it was a straight case of a gastric hemorrhage, a common problem in this area. I gave him plenty of sedation, a few pints of blood, intravenous feedings, and he quieted down. I kept Neil in the hospital for a while and then allowed him to go home on a special diet with special medication. I wanted to build up his general health before doing a gastrectomy on him.

On September 11, 1955, we removed his stomach. He was in quite good shape by that time, but I didn't want to see him ever have another hemorrhage as massive as that one in July.

The following spring, Neil became quite lame with a pain in his back and in one leg. I sent him on to Halifax, where he had two discs removed. Neil says his back is as good as new now and he's had no trouble since then. I think he still enjoys a little party once in a while too!

On the evening of April 1, 1948, Mr. and Mrs. R. J. MacDonald went out visiting. Considering that she was six months pregnant, she seemed perfectly well. In those days during the winter months, women living down in the country didn't get their prenatal examinations as regularly as they should. They had to depend on the doctor being in their area. If there was a woman expecting a baby, the doctor always called while passing through the neighborhood and gave a prenatal examination. But during that year, I hadn't been down their way during the daytime for some time. Mrs. R. J. hadn't seen me since she was three months pregnant.

Mr. and Mrs. MacDonald arrived home sometime that evening

and went to bed. Later R. J. woke up to find his wife in convulsions. He had to go about a quarter of a mile to call me. I was in Boulardarie Centre, but as usual one of the telephone operators found me and explained the case. I had to go to Baddeck first to replenish my maternity bag just in case I might have to do a delivery.

When I arrived at the home I found that Mrs. MacDonald was not in labor but was unconscious and having intermittent convulsions. It was a really desperate case. I injected an anticonvulsive medication and we made arrangements to take her to North Sydney Hospital. At about eight in the morning, with the patient still unconscious, we started out. The roads were terrible. "It was like going through soup," R. J. remembers. "We'd start down into a hole not knowing if we were going to come up or not."

After Mrs. MacDonald had been in the hospital for a few days, she quieted down. In hope of getting a live baby, she was discharged from the hospital but ordered to stay in North Sydney, handy to the hospital. She remained there almost a month, but then she went into convulsions again. She was taken to the hospital immediately and a Caesarian section done, but the baby could not be saved.

Their second child was born on June 28, 1950. This time I watched her very carefully, with regular prenatal examinations. She began to develop trouble in the seventh month, some albumin and a little high pressure. In those days there weren't the drugs available to control these symptoms that doctors use today. It was a matter of diet, watching the case closely, and saying your prayers, hoping the mother would go into labor before she'd go into convulsions. This time she went to full term. Her blood pressure was a little high and she had considerable albumin. By this time, we had the hospital open in Baddeck and she was brought there. She started labor, a little slow, but I felt quite safe about her.

I was called to Middle River on an emergency. It was only twelve miles away and I figured I had plenty of time to get out there and back because her labor was going slowly. While I was gone Mrs. MacDonald went into convulsions again. I hurried back quickly.

By the time I got back to Baddeck, the nurses had Mrs. MacDonald in the delivery room. They had called Dr. Tabby Bethune who was home for a few days' vacation. Dr. Tabby was Administrator of Victoria General Hospital in Halifax, but he had been trained in anesthetics prior to the war years. He responded immediately to the nurse's call, and by the time I arrived he had controlled her convulsions by giving her complete anesthesia. The cervix was well dilated. I put instruments on and delivered her without any trouble. The baby and mother were well.

The MacDonalds' next child was Calvin, born May 18, 1951. This time the mother didn't begin to show any albumin or high pressure until she was into the eighth month. She had watched her diet and she came up to Baddeck to stay at the Alderwood Home next to the hospital, and had a normal delivery.

When Gordon was born on September 1, 1957, Mrs. MacDonald went full term and had no trouble at all. Ann was born September 1, 1958, but again Mrs. MacDonald had trouble with albumin and a little high pressure. I wanted her to go to the hospital, but she refused. I was a little cross with her, and she was a little cross with me for wanting her to go. She went on a salt-free diet for two months, eating nothing but milk and fruit from the seventh month to the ninth and lost a lot of weight, and when she came in for delivery she was normal. But fifteen minutes following the delivery, after we got her back into the war, she collapsed. Her pressure went down, down, down. We managed to bring it back up again, but I sweated gumdrops in those twenty or thirty minutes.

Angus Roderick was born January 5, 1961, and Mrs. Mac-Donald carried the child to term and stayed home until the very last minute. With her history I would have been happier to have her in town near the hospital. The day she went into labor was a stormy one, but the storm eased just as she left home for the hospital. The moment she arrived at the hospital, the snow started again, worse than ever. I'm happy to report that everything went well at that delivery.

On the evening of January 8, 1930, I received a call to the home of Mrs. Dan Matheson in Breton Cove. This was the third trip that I had made north without having had sleep, so I was tired. But she was in labor, so I started out.

I fell asleep behind the horse in the sleigh, just as I was passing the Post Office in Baddeck, and when I awoke I was well up Rocky-side, between South Gut and Englishtown, which meant I had slept while the horse travelled about fifteen miles.

At Englishtown I stabled my horse in Allan MacLean's and Allan ferried me across the mouth of St. Ann's Harbour. At the other side I found Dan W. MacLeod, who had been sent to meet me. It was then I realized my horse must have walked the fifteen miles while I was asleep. "Where were you?" Dan asked. "I've been waiting for an hour."

Dan had a real good roadster of which he was very proud, when he turned his rig towards home we made up for some lost time, arriving at Matheson's about midnight. I was a little late. The baby had been born about a half hour before I arrived: a girl, and already named after the nurse in attendance, Mrs. Hannah Matheson.

Hannah, the baby born that night, had a very rough childhood. At the age of fourteen, she began to develop synovitis in the right knee joint. I thought at first it might be from an injury, but when the second knee joint began to swell, I knew I was dealing with a rheumatoid condition.

At one time during her teens in September of 1947, she reached the point where she was completely unable to get out of bed. I sent her over to North Sydney hospital, where she spent ten weeks with casts on both legs. Her general health improved considerably during that period. When she returned home, she was in bed for another six months. While these casts were still on, near Christmas of that year, she had an acute flare-up. There was a heavy snowstorm raging, and her family waited until it abated a little before calling me. It was Christmas night when they phoned.

I got away by horse and sleigh very early the next morning and arrived at her home, thirty-five miles away, at eight that night. I was eleven hours making the trip because of the bad road conditions.

The only relief I could give her was to slit both casts to take the pressure off the swelling. I went down a week later and removed both casts and put on new ones. Later, when these were removed, Hannah had to learn to walk all over again with crutches. She tried, but she was greatly discouraged, and I'm sure she did not put the most into her exercises to keep the muscles in good condition. As a result there was further deterioration.

This was about the time when cortisone was first being used in treating rheumatoid arthritis. In 1951 I sent Hannah to the Victoria General Hospital in Halifax. I went down shortly after and talked to the specialist who was attending her. He told me he considered that her rheumatoid condition was "burnt out," meaning it was inactive and that the only treatment she needed was physiotherapy. I asked him what he planned to do. He said he planned to send her home, as they had no physiotherapists there to do that type of work. I knew what that meant. It meant that the girl would be condemned to complete invalidism for the rest of her life.

By this time she was again just a bed case and not able to walk, even with crutches. I asked the specialist if there was any place in Nova Scotia where she could get physiotherapy. He told me the only place for physiotherapy was at Camp Hill Hospital, a military hospital in Halifax, and it would be impossible to get her in there.

I visited Camp Hill Hospital and talked with Dr. Kirk, I knew well. He was very sympathetic and thought perhaps something could be arranged. He said it would cost nine dollars a day for the therapy. "We can't take her in this hospital," he told me, "but if the Victoria General will keep her there and send her up every morning by ambulance, she can get a treatment here every day, and they can come and take her back at night." I talked with him a little more and he made an even better offer. "Look" he said, "I'll tell you what we'll do. If you can get the V.G. to send her up every morning for treatment, we'll see that she gets her treatment, and we won't even put it on the books." That was what I'd been hoping for. I went back to V.G. and talked it over with Dr. Clarence Bethune. He agreed that the hospital would do it.

Hannah spent two months there, being transported by ambulance daily, with the result that when she came home she was able to walk, using two canes. This was a vast improvement.

She got along about ten years or more in this fashion. Then once again there was a gradual degeneration of her joints. Finally she became incapacitated to the point where her knees were both flexed and frozen at a right angle and she could not get out of bed by herself. She had to be lifted into a chair and lifted from the chair back to bed again.

In 1966 I had her brought in to our hospital in Baddeck and called Dr. Austin MacDonald of Sydney in for consultation. Dr. Austin is an internist and a rheumatoid specialist. He told me she could have surgery and have both knees straightened, enabling her to walk again. He said that it would take a great deal of courage and effort on her part in order that these operations be successful. He had mental reservations as to whether Hannah had the motivation, or would put the effort into the physiotherapy that would be necessary following the surgery.

It took a month or more of talking to Hannah every chance I got before she finally consented. When she did give in, she said it was only to please me.

There was a waiting period of some months, and it was May of 1967 before she was admitted to the Victoria General Hospital. First she had the right knee operated on. The leg was straightened and the joint ankylosed, that is, frozen so it would not bend. One month later, surgery was performed on the left knee. The leg was straightened and an artificial joint put in. These two operations were followed by several months of physiotherapy.

Before Hannah left the hospital, she was taken into a clinic, where there were residents, surgeons, and interns, and she was shown off to them as an example of what could be done for advanced cases of arthritis if the patient had the will, courage, and motivation to go ahead and have the work done. This gave Hannah's morale a great boost.

She walks quite nicely now, using two canes. This is a far different situation than before she had the surgery done. She can get in and out of bed by herself; she can dress herself; and she can get around reasonably well. She tells me that "some days I walk two miles in the house," and she's very proud of it.

12

TRAINS, BOATS, PLANES, AND OTHER PROBLEMS

I said I would tell the story of my plane trip to Ingonish during the winter of 1934, and that's as good a place as any to start this chapter on some of the really unusual trips I have made through the years.

I had been in Big Baddeck when the hurry-up call came from Ingonish. A woman had been in labor for three days and my services were urgently needed. I knew it would be a two- or three-day trip by horse and sleigh to get to her, so I phoned the Cape Breton Flying Club and asked them to have a plane meet me in Baddeck to fly me to Ingonish.

I went back to the office to replenish my bags and then went down to the ice in front of the Yacht Club and boarded the plane. In these days the planes they used were open; it was like sitting in a horse-drawn sleigh, with just a windshield ahead of you. The pilot didn't think it was necessary on such a short trip to fasten a seat belt. He just told me, "Make sure your arms don't get in the way. Don't close those throttles with your elbows." It was a dual control machine, used for teaching.

We were flying over South Gut Glen when I looked down and saw that we were going by Alex Miley MacLeod's house. I realized that Mrs. MacLeod was expecting and due about then. I said to myself, "I hope she doesn't decide to have that baby tonight," but I learned later that she did.

Right at the time we were flying over the MacLeod's house, the engine of the plane conked out. The pilot had to glide quite a long way. He just barely missed the chimneys of some houses in trying to make the ice at St. Ann's. But he landed the plane on St. Ann's Bay, right near the brook, where even though the temperature was eighteen below zero, the ice was very slushy.

We got out and the pilot took the gas line apart. He found that water in the gas had turned into ice, causing the engine to stop. He fixed it up and said to me, "Get in." I didn't know whether to get back in again or not, but decided there was no choice. I crawled back into my seat. And then we couldn't get the plane off the ground. The skis had frozen in the slush. We got out again, and each of us got on a wing, jumping up and down to loosen the plane from the slush. After a while we got it out and away we went again.

Everything was smooth until we got over Smoky Mountain. Then we began to get into some downdrafts. The plane would drop 150 feet at a time; it would drop, and then he'd climb; it would drop again, and he'd climb again. I don't know how many times it dropped, but every time the plane dropped, I'd leave the seat. I was holding onto the dashboard with the tips of my fingers, and when the plane would drop, I'd jackknife with my rear sticking away out of the plane and my head down. Then when the plane would settle again, I'd come right back into my seat.

When I was talking to Ingonish earlier that day, I was told to land on Freshwater Lake, but I probably didn't pay too much attention to what I was told. When we got over Smoky and I spotted Ingonish Harbour, I said, "There's the place for us to land." Freshwater Lake would have been much handier to where we were going. Not only that, but a much easier landing. To get down to Ingonish Harbour meant circling several times, but we finally got there.

When I got out of the plane I swore I'd never get in another one. But the next morning I was damn glad to get the plane to come back after me. This trip, to avoid the downdrafts over Smoky, the pilot went out to sea quite a distance. When I looked down and saw the water and thin ice, I wondered whether our chances were really better over the open water than over the mountain with the downdrafts: I was grateful for the pilot's help, but that certainly wasn't my favorite way to travel!

Another frightening trip was one I made on foot across the railroad bridge at Grand Narrows. If the wind and water were too rough for the ferry to operate, the only way to get from one side to the other was to cross on the railroad bridge. I did that many times over the years. I would usually check with the operator in the railway station first to make sure there was no train coming.

But one day I was in a hurry, and I didn't check the train schedule. I was halfway across the bridge when a train came along. There was no room for both the train and me on the bridge. I knew the train wouldn't get off the track, so I crawled out on the outside of one of the girders and hung on until the train went by. I thought I was going to be shaken off. I had my arms wrapped around the girder and held a medical bag in each hand. I have forgotten everything about that trip, where I was going and whom I was going to see. Everything has faded away from my memory except how hard it was to hold on and how glad I was when the train passed. I'm sure I couldn't have held on much longer than I did; and the water down below looked very cold.

Archie MacIvor reminded me recently of another travel episode I had forgotten. His sister, Ann, was the public health nurse at that time and went with me on confinement cases.

In the middle of January 1950 Ann and I had to get across the lake to Washabuck. A woman who worked as cook in a lumber camp there was in labor. She had made arrangements to come to the Baddeck hospital for delivery, but labor had started prematurely and on a terrible day. There was a gale blowing from the east and it was raining hard. Though it was January, the lake had not yet frozen. Because of the high winds and rough water getting across to Washabuck by rowboat or even a motor boat was impossible. Finally I was able to persuade Captain Dannie Murdock MacDonald to gather up his crew and take Ann and me to MacKay's Point in the government mail boat.

We made the crossing easily enough, but when we reached the other side, the seas were running so high and the wind so strong, we were unable to stop at the wharf. The captain told us that as long as he could keep the boat running at full speed, he could pass fairly close to the head of the wharf. On the first pass, we threw our bags ashore. I perched on the rail for the second pass. Once I let go I didn't have much choice. The roll of the boat threw me in the air and waiting hands grabbed me as my feet hit the end of the wharf. On the third pass Ann leaped gracefully and landed with a good margin of safety.

During this time Archie was trying to keep his mother calm. Washabuck and South Cove were on the same party-line telephone circuit, so they kept track of our progress. Archie remembers that when they learned we were on our way, "Mother just couldn't sit still. She was back and forth saying, 'They'll never get there. They'll never get there.' And, 'That boat is going to be swamped before they reach Washabuck.' While you and Ann were crossing to Washabuck, mother must have walked miles up and down the kitchen floor. But at last we got word on the telephone that you and Ann had landed. Then she started worrying about your getting back."

We were met at the wharf by Pete Northen, whose wife was the patient. The temporary camp they were living in at the time was by no means an ideal place for a complicated case.

A prenatal hemorrhage in an isolated country area always strikes fear into the heart of a doctor. There was no God's way to move the patient that day into a hospital. Come what may, we were on our own. Fortunately the bleeding that had been so alarming at first was caused by some separation of a marginal placenta previa (after-birth implanted low in the womb), which nature, with the help of some medication, took care of as labor progressed. Mother and baby did fine.

Archie continued his story: "We waited all afternoon and every time the phone rang we listened in if it was a Washabuck ring or a Central ring, to find out if you were going to try to get back that day. Mother kept saying, 'No. They won't try to make it back. They will never get back in this storm,' and she kept pacing the floor. At last we heard on the phone that the doctor and Ann had left and were headed toward Baddeck."

By the time we were ready to go home, the storm had eased off somewhat, but not enough for the boat to stop at the wharf. On the first pass, we threw our bags aboard; on the second and third passes we jumped. We felt like veterans at this sort of thing by now.

Sometimes in early winter, before the ice had frozen solid on the lake, we would have an added complication, with ice near the shore and open water in the middle. One such time came when I was called to John Allan MacNeil's at MacNeil's Vale in the mountain back of Boulacet Harbour.

Red Rory and his son Joe Red Rory said they would come to get me in the small government ferry. They had taken their motor out for the winter but figured they could row across. First they had to haul the boat from the shore out to Allan's (Bone) Island on the ice, and then put the boat in the water there. Meanwhile I walked across the ice from Baddeck to Kidston's Island to meet them. We rowed back to Allan's Island, pulled the boat up there and walked the ice to Red Rory's house, where there was a driver waiting for me.

Coming back, the whole order of traveling was reversed, but by this time the wind had died down and ice had formed between Allan's Island and Kidston's Island. We took a third man with us, Quentin MacDonald. He stood in the bow of the boat with an oar and broke the ice in front of us and on the sides, so Joe and Red Rory could use their oars to row. It was slow motion, but they finally landed me on Kidston's Island just about daybreak, and I walked home from there.

No matter how bad the weather or how late the hour, I could always find someone to help me get to a patient or home again. One man who pulled me out of a number of mudholes or snowbanks was Colin Nicholson of Big Baddeck. One time I had been called to see Mrs. MacKenzie at Baddeck Forks in the middle of the winter. The road was bad, extremely icy, with snowbanks on the sides of the road. It was impossible to keep a car on the road and I didn't. I piled into a snowbank and stuck solid. I was only about a mile from Colin's house so I headed there.

Colin remembers that he was awakened by a noise downstairs. "It was half-past two on a Monday morning, New Year's Day 1937. Everybody was in bed and I heard somebody, so I got up. There was the doctor in the kitchen. He told me he was stuck in the snow. There were no electric lights at that time, so I had to light the lantern, go out to the barn, harness up a team of horses, hitch them to the sleigh, and away we went. It was just over a mile to the car, and we hooked up the horses to it. We couldn't budge it, it was so buried. The doctor said, 'I'll have to put the air under it.' So he got out his jack and raised up the tail end a little bit, and then the horses pulled it out. It was hard pulling—about as hard as the tooth the doctor had pulled for me the week before. I remember he said he was sorry he had charged me for pulling the tooth. I told him there might be another tooth some time, and he said, 'All right. Remind me of it.' "

The spring break-up was another real problem each year. Before modern roads and snowplowing, the most miserable time of year for travel was in the spring, when you couldn't use a sleigh because of bare roads and mud, and yet there were still so many snowbanks that it was almost impossible to use the wagon or the car. Sometimes I would start out with horse and wagon, change the wagon for a sleigh, then back to wagon again. When the snowbanks were completely gone, I could use a wagon all the way. Almost invariably, these calls would be at night in rainstorms. I would be ten or twelve hours in a wagon, making a trip to North Shore. Starting out, I would try to keep the rain from running down my neck, keeping the "buffalo" wrapped around me so the cushions would be dry. But within an hour the rain would be pouring down my neck and I would be sitting in a puddle of water.

In the early years, we wouldn't start out with a car until the last snowbank had melted away and the rest of the road was beginning to get dry and dusty. However, with the pressure of increasing calls, when most of the roads were dry but there were still some snowbanks left, I would take a car and spend a good part of the night shoveling.

I recall a trip I had to Wreck Cove by car one spring. Just as I was going out the door I met three of the boys who worked at the Royal Bank. One of them was a MacIntosh; I forget who the other two were. I asked them if they would like to come for a drive. "Sure," they said and jumped in. I felt a little guilty, as they were all dressed up in their banking clothes, and I knew if we got into any mudhouse they'd be a mess before we got back.

Going down Baddeck Bay, we got along fairly well. Whenever I'd see a soft spot in the road, I'd put my car in low gear and drive about fifty miles per hour. Whenever she'd hit those mudholes, she'd bounce out. But on MacAulay's hill, we bogged right down and had to get out of the car. At first the boys tried to protect their good clothes as well as they could, jumping from rock to rock. We finally got some fence poles and a large rock, and using the rock for a fulcrum and the fence poles for a pry, we would pry the wheels up and get some stones under them. Then we'd move ahead a few feet and do the same thing over again. It probably took us an hour to get up MacAulay's Hill.

Just where the road turns off to Big Harbour, we went down so badly in the mud that we couldn't open the car doors. The chap by the name of MacIntosh got out first. He went out through the window and when he got out, he went down in the mud and stuck. He couldn't move at all. The rest of us crawled out of the window and lay down on top of the car. We got MacIntosh by the shoulders and pulled for all we were worth. Finally, up he came, leaving his shoes in the mud. I'm sure they're still there.

By this time we weren't paying any more attention to trying to keep our clothes clean. We were hopelessly covered with mud. We stood around trying to figure out how we were going to get the car out. Just then, Jim MacKillop came out of the woods with a pair of horses pulling a set of bob sleighs. I'm sure each one of those horses weighed 1,800 pounds. Jim disconnected the hind bob sleigh, took a chain and wrapped it around the front sleigh, which he left hitched to the horses. The other end of the chain he attached to the car. The horses tried mightily to pull the car out, but the harder the horses pulled, the deeper the front wheel seemed to sink into mud. Finally we pried up the front part of the car, got rocks and pieces of logs under the wheels, and backed the bob sleigh right in under the front end of the car. Then we took the front wheels off the car and let the car rest right on the bob sleigh. This tactic worked and we got the car out of the mudhole.

From there on we didn't do too badly. We got to Wreck Cove some time around six or seven that evening, made our call, and started home again. By that time the temperature had dropped, so there was a little frost in the ground and we didn't have nearly as much trouble. I believe we were home before two o'clock in the morning. In early spring, although the days were warm, the nights were cold and the ground would harden up enough to carry the car. There was always a certain amount of guesswork involved in deciding how to travel during the spring break-up. And no matter which way you decided to go, you usually wished you hadn't.

This next story, one I've always thought of as "the Ambrose Hall story," is such a classic that I gave it that title long before I ever thought of gathering these stories together.

I received a call late one evening towards the end of April 1936 to go see Ambrose Hall, who was then staying with Jimmie Edward MacLeod at St. Patrick's Channel. It was another one of those calls when there was so much excitement on the other end of the line that I couldn't get much information. All I found out was that Ambrose Hall was very sick and needed a doctor in a hurry.

After I hung up the receiver, I asked myself how I was going to get to St. Patrick's Channel in a hurry. Jimmie Edward's home was about thirteen miles west of Baddeck on the main road, then known as Route No.5. (It's now the Trans-Canada Highway and is a beautiful, wide, all-year-round highway.)

That evening I knew that the road was muddy and bare of snow all the way, except for the snowbank at Johnny Sandy's. It was still five to seven feet high, and in the middle of an uphill grade. I could take the main road to Middle River, as far as the foot of Hunter's Mountain, turn left on the Buckwheat road and hit Route No. 5 at the other end of the snowbank. The hitch with this plan was that there was also one snowbank on this road. This snowbank was also five to seven feet deep, but on a downhill grade. The road had been well-packed all winter and a few nights before I had sneaked my car over the top of this snowbank quite successfully. I thought I might be able to do it again.

Unfortunately, it didn't work. There had been a couple of warm days since the previous trip and the snow had softened some. The snowbank was almost a quarter of a mile long. I very carefully eased my car into the sled tracks and moved very slowly. About three-quarters of the way over the bank there was a slope, and my car left the track and sank down in the snow, I worked hard with my shovel for two hours, but only succeeded in getting the car in deeper.

I gave up, took my bags with me, and walked back to Baddeck. There I borrowed another car and started the trip again up the shore road. By this time it was one o'clock in the morning. When I reached Johnny Sandy's snowbank, I realized there was no use trying to drive the car over. I got out my shovel and said to myself, "I will have this snowbank shoveled for this year anyway. I'll probably be using this road again before the snow melts anyway."

It was just ten o'clock in the morning when I finished, about twelve hours after the hurry-up call to see Ambrose. I stopped at Donald Smith's store in Nyanza to find out whether the man I was going to see was still alive. If he were dead, I might as well turn back. After shoveling snow for twelve hours I was tired.

I walked into the store and what did I see? I saw Ambrose Hall doing his morning shopping. I asked him, "Ambrose, how are you feeling?" "Fine," he said. I turned around, walked out of the store, and drove home.

In the early years a trip over Barrachois Mountain was always a problem in winter or spring, whether by car, horse and sleigh, or wagon. The present road is a wide, paved one, fairly low on the mountain. The old road went quite high up, and then down again, and it was always icy in the spring of the year.

Allan MacLean and his brother Everett reminded me of a time they helped me get through the Barrachois Mountain. I knew there was a lot of ice there, but it was urgent that I get down to the North Shore, so I stopped to pick up a few friends at Tarbot to help me get through. Allan and Everett, D. J. Smith, and Dannie Holy MacDonald said they would help.

Allan recalls the story: "We started that day and got to the foot of the mountain, and then we told the doctor, 'We can't get through.' But he just said, 'I'm going through. I'm going through.'

"Well, we started, pushing and shoveling; we had an ax and we were cutting trenches in the ice along the high side of the road so the car wouldn't slip. We got as far as the spring and that was the trouble. There was nothing but the high hill above, and ice down across the road at a severe angle. Over the mountain you would go if you ever slipped. We said, 'This is it; we can't go any further.' But the doctor said, 'I'm going through; I have to go down North Shore and I'm not going to turn back.'

"So we started again with the ax. We cut another trench in the ice on the high side of the road all the way through to bare ground. By dark that evening we had got the doctor as far as the bridge. There was no stopping him. That was the first car to go through that spring. There was an old wooden rail along the road, and if the car had gone over that, it would drop four or five hundred feet and land right in the middle of the river."

When I talked with Allan and Everett recently about that trip, I said to them, "I suppose I gave each of you ten dollars for that trip." Allan replied, "No, you didn't give us a damn cent. We didn't want anything and we weren't looking for anything, either." It was an example of the kind of help the country doctor got from the local people along the route.

My son, Carleton Lamont, now known as "Dr. Monty," used to enjoy making trips with me, but wasn't often allowed to go. When I took off for a call in the country, it might be a day or two before I could return, and of course he had school to worry about. One trip he did make with me is still vivid in his mind. Here is the way he recalls it:

"I remember leaving Baddeck with Father about one o'clock in the afternoon. It was in the spring of 1942 and we had to make a call on the North Shore. I remember he was driving a 1941 Pontiac at the time. We left Baddeck on relatively good roads and reached St. Ann's with no difficulty about one-thirty. The next seven miles took us until eight-thirty in the evening.

"We had gone only a few hundred feet from St. Ann's when we were hopelessly mired in the mud. As usual, several men soon came on the scene with axes. They cut some spruce boughs from the side of the road, jacked the car up, put rocks under the wheels, and with the spruce boughs spread before us, we managed to straddle the mudhole. We were in another one within another few hundred yards, and so it continued. As we got along a couple of miles, we realized that by this time there were at least seven or eight men with us and each time we got stuck, each grabbed hold on a separate corner of the car and lifted us out of the mudhole. About halfway through to Englishtown, the men decided that the road the rest of the way was quite clear and let us go on our own. However, before we had gone very far, we were stuck again. This time we were helped by a group of several men who had walked up from Englishtown, knowing we were on the way north and would be needing help.

"They carried on, lifting us from one mudhole to the other. We got across the Englishtown ferry without difficulty. We were on fairly good road down through Jersey Cove when we spied a bad spot ahead. Father asked me to get out and walk through this mudhole just to see how deep it was. Fortunately, I had on a pair of low rubber boots, with no laces. As I walked through the mudhole with the mud just to the tops of my boots, which would be about to my knees, I heard a great roar behind me and looked back. To my horror, Father was driving forward at a great rate of speed in first gear, expecting me to jump out of the way. I tried to run, but my boots held fast, so I was forced to jump and leave the boots in the mud. Father went by at about forty miles an hour, bouncing from one bank to the other. By the time he got through this mudhole, which was about two hundred feet long, he had not only chewed up my rubber boots, but also dented all four mudguards on the car."

We finally reached our destination late that night and, as usual, the telephone rang several times. Out in the country like that, everyone on the party line knew the doctor was in the neighborhood, and if they had something bothering them, not serious enough to call me down on a separate trip, they would call and ask me to stop in while I was in the area.

Monty remembers that we answered another call that night: "As soon as father finished with his patient, we had to set out again farther away from home. Since the road was bad, this time we had a horse and wagon. I believe we were going to see Collie MacInnis in Breton Cove, about two miles further down the road. That trip is very vivid. Father sat in the front seat of the wagon with the driver and I sat in the back. The horse loped along, and since it was a spring-fitted wagon, I was many times in the air and back down again on the sharp edge of the wagon. I might say my posterior aspect was rather blue by the time we reached our destination."

We got into trouble another time when Monty was with me, though this time we were not answering a medical call. We needed some hardwood for our fireplace, so we set off driving on the ice along the shoreline, looking for a good stand of suitable trees. This was probably about 1944, because I remember we had a second-hand coupe with a very large trunk. New cars were hard to come by then because of the war.

Monty remembers that we drove along until we found a fine grove of young birch trees. "We spent an hour or so, Father of course doing most of the work with his saw and ax. He cut down several trees and cut them into lengths that would fit into the trunk of the car. When the trunk was well filled, overloaded actually, we headed for home. Unfortunately, an area we had crossed on the way up proved to be a pond on the ice, and with the extra weight of the logs, we broke through. I heard an earsplitting shattering noise and then Father screamed at me to jump out of the car. I opened my door, and indeed we were going through the ice. I saw nothing but cold water below the open door. I managed to scramble out onto solid ice. I looked back to see my father sitting in the car, with the door open, gazing down into the water as the car slowly settled almost out of sight. He realized this was a pond and that somewhere there must be a bottom. As I recall, the car settled until the water level was just below the front window. At this point, Father crawled blithely through the window and out onto the edge of the ice.

"I was immediately dispatched to a nearby house on the shore where several men gathered together a bunch of hardwood poles. With these they managed to break the surface ice until they came to the edge of the pond Father's car was in. At this point they brought up a team of horses, which they hitched to the front of the car. The team pulled and the car came out of the waterhole, none the worse for wear. We even managed to get the car home that night."

Not all the danger and close calls were the result of the elements or travel conditions. Extreme fatigue was sometimes my worst enemy.

On a rainy summer evening in 1946 I was called to White Point, north of Ingonish. Dr. Austin MacDonald who served that part of Cape Breton was away on vacation. I stopped in Ingonish and picked up the public health nurse, Miss Isabel MacKinnon, to help me. But the patient, John Willie MacKinnon, died before morning from a ruptured aneurism at the base of his brain. About two in the morning, in pouring rain, we set out for home. While driving through the community of Smelt Brook, I hit some puddles, the distributor got wet, and the engine conked out. I woke some fishermen and they got out of bed and came to help. There were at least six of them with their heads under the hood of the car. They took the distributor apart, pulling off the wires until I wondered how in the world they were ever going to get them back on properly. But I underestimated them; their experience with marine engines stood them in good stead. They dried out the distributor, put the wiring back in place, and away we went.

I dropped Isabel off at her home in Ingonish and started up Smoky. I realized I was very sleepy and having trouble staying awake. By the time I hit the top of Smoky and started down, I was suddenly aware that I could hear myself snoring. The left front wheel of the car was just over the edge of the road. I remember saying to myself, "Now, that gave me such a fright that I won't go to sleep again; clear fright will keep me awake." But I hadn't driven twenty feet when I heard myself snoring again. This business of going to sleep at the wheel happened many times. I found that when I fell asleep my foot relaxed and let up on the accelerator. Then the different sound of the engine would wake me up.

After the second time that happened, I realized I should pull to the side of the road and have a sleep. But my experience in sleeping in the car, even in the summer, was that I always woke up in chills. I wanted to get down to the foot of the mountain and get home where I could sleep. But it was impossible for me to stay awake. I finally said to myself, "Well, I have to get down this mountain." I put the car in low gear and I let myself go, keeping my right eye open. In this way, I got down the mountain.

There wasn't a single house along the shore where I couldn't have knocked at the door and been invited in for a sleep. But I was so sleepy I'd be past a house before I'd recognize where I was. In this manner, I continued to D. B. MacLeod's home and turned in there. Mrs. MacLeod, an old lady, woke up and let me in. It was during the summer and her house was full. There wasn't an empty bed, but the old lady got out of bed and gave me hers. Where she spent the rest of the night, I don't know.

That was one time I didn't phone home or even the Englishtown Central to report where I was. I just dropped on the bed, went sound asleep, and didn't wake until ten in the morning.

Fatigue is a strange thing: Sometimes it gets you and you can't shake it; other times you can forget about it, at least for a while.

In March 17, 1948, I was called to Donald Garrett MacDonald's at North River Meadow. When I reached their home I discovered that Mrs. MacDonald had been in heavy labor for twelve hours.

During her prenatal period, I had told her I would not deliver any more children for her at home. Her first two confinements had been very difficult, and this time I had planned to take her to North Sydney Hospital for Caesarean section at the first sign of labor.

On examination I found the neck of the womb was completely dilated, with the baby's head still high in the pelvis. However, the presentation was normal. I delivered the baby by high forceps, and found her a very cooperative patient.

After that delivery I was extremely fatigued. I had been on the go three days and nights without any sleep and decided to spend the night there. But I was afraid that, because of my extreme tiredness, I'd be unable to sleep, so I took three grains of Nembutal to make sure. Just as I was falling asleep, the telephone rang. It was a call to go to Whycocomagh, fifty miles away, to see Dr. Ferguson, who had fallen and broken a leg.

Donald harnessed the horse to the sleigh and drove me to North River Bridge where I had left my car. He said I was so dopey I could hardly sit in the sleigh and I slept most of the way in. Once I got into the car, however, I was all right. I snapped out of it and drove without any problem. Dr. Ferguson, it turned out, had a fracture of the tibia, and the alignment was good. I put the leg up in a plaster of Paris splint and advised him to over to Inverness the next day for x-ray to make sure all was well.

By this time the excitement of the hurried trip to Whycocomagh was wearing off, and I was again so tired I wondered how I was going to drive home. Dr. Ferguson said, "I can offer you a strong cup of coffee, or, if you wish, a drink of rum." I took the rum, tossed it off, and drove home. I felt fine by this time. Breakfast was on the table. I had a shave and wash and started off on a round of country calls that had accumulated during the night.

13

SUNDAYS, CELEBRITIES, AND RUM-RUNNING

*S*unday was always my busiest day. This was especially true during the earlier years, but it continued to some extent all during the time I was in practice, at least up until the 'sixties. Sunday, August 7, 1938, was, I think, the busiest day I ever had.

The first patient I took in that day was Marion MacDermid of Beinn Breagh. She was working at the home of Dr. Gilbert Grosvenor, the President of the National Geographic Society. The Grosvenor family had been out sailing on the lake in their yacht "Elsie" when Marian developed some abdominal pain. She continued working despite the pain until her father learned of it and called me about eleven in the morning. Because I had some patients in the office, it was an hour or so before I got over there to see her.

As soon as I saw her, I put her in my car and headed for North Sydney Hospital. She had acute appendicitis, almost gangrenous. By two in the afternoon, she was in the operating room. Marian remembers that just as she was waking up, coming out of the anesthetic, she heard my voice in the ward. I asked her, "How are you Marian?" and she replied "I'm fine but I haven't had my appendix out yet."

Then I told her, "Put your hand down and feel your stomach and you'll find that you have had it out."

"By gosh," she said, "I guess I did, but I didn't know it." Then she asked me, "What are you doing still here now if I've had my appendix out?"

"Oh," I said, "I've been home and I'm back with another case for the O.R." It was Marian's impression that this was late in the afternoon, but, as I said, she was just coming out of the anesthetic.

That second patient was Mrs. Kennie MacQueen of Birch Plain, who had a ruptured ovarian cyst with considerable hemorrhaging. Mrs. MacQueen was admitted to the hospital at ten-thirty that night, which probably means that it was midnight or so before we got to the O.R., and almost morning before I got home.

The following Tuesday, August 9, I still had not slept. On that day, Sadie Buchanan of the Hotel Baddeck developed some abdominal pain. I had gone to Iona Monday evening and hadn't yet returned. When I did, about six o'clock in the evening, I went to see Sadie immediately. She, too, had acute appendicitis, and I put her in my car and headed for the hospital. Over the years those three days have run together in my mind, until I was sure I had taken three emergency cases to North Sydney Hospital on the same day! My confusion is understandable since I hadn't been to bed at all during that time.

Not all of my patients were people. Alex Kerr of North River recently recalled a time when I doctored their horse "We had a real sick horse at home. I went to the barn Monday morning and the horse was lying down sick and couldn't get up. Myself and all the other 'quack horse doctors' around were giving the old horse everything we could think of to see if we could get him around. We were having very little success and finally we put a sling around him and lifted him up so he wouldn't blister too badly. He still wasn't getting any better.

"My brother, Johnny, was working for Gordon MacAulay in Baddeck at the time. He saw Dr. MacMillan on the street and he was telling the doctor about the horse. The doctor told Johnny to come into the office and he'd mix something to give the horse. Johnny sent it down in the mail to us. It was only a small bottle and the directions read, 'Half at once and four hours later, the rest of the bottle.' I gave the horse half the bottle that afternoon when the mail came and four hours later I went down to the barn. I didn't know if he'd be dead or alive. When I got to the barn the horse was standing up eating and that was the first time he had stood on his feet for a whole week."

I can't remember what I concluded was wrong with the horse or what medicine I sent out, but apparently it worked. There was no veterinary doctor in the area at that time and I was always glad to help the farmers out if I could.

In the Nyanza Indian village ten miles west of Baddeck lived Mrs. Victoria Francis, who helped me for many years. Although she wasn't a trained nurse, she was a skilled midwife and had a "nursing instinct" that brought comfort to many sick people of the village. I was always glad to have her with me on a case. Victoria had no Indian blood at all. She had been born of a poor white family who already had more children than they could feed, so they had given her to an Indian family who were better off.

Over the years, I've spent many a night in the Indian village waiting for a maternity case to be delivered. In the summertime, if I had to wait very long, I might go out in the car and try to get some sleep. During cold weather I would take off my top coat, roll it into a pillow, lie down on the floor of the cabin, and fall sound asleep, with Victoria on one side of me and "Little Annie" Pierro on the other. Quite often, when the patient would get restless I'd suggest to her, especially if I were very tired, that it would be better if she got up and walked around to hurry things a bit. I had my doubts whether it really did hurry the delivery, but that seemed to be the accepted opinion at that time, and besides her bed was usually the only one in the house. As soon as she got up, I'd lie down on the bed and go to sleep. After a while I'd wake with Victoria poking me in the ribs with her thumb, "Malbalaywit (Doctor), get up. Baby coming." So I'd get up out of the bed and scrub as best I could while the patient got back into the bed. Then I'd deliver the baby, look after everything that needed attention, and then go home.

One of my very early experiences in the Indian Village was a sad one. Victoria wasn't with me that time, but I wish she had been. A few months after I opened practice in Baddeck I was called to Nyanza to see Mrs. Charlie Pierro. She was pregnant and not feeling well. On examination I found she had valvular heart disease, and by the time she was six months along, I had to start her on digitalis. I was concerned about her delivery. When labor began, I was called to Nyanza. Katie Pierro, a relative of the family, was the midwife and she wanted no part of having a Doctor there for the delivery. She just wanted me to examine the patient to determine whether she was really in labor. Then she told me, "Me midwife. Me no want doctor. Me just want to know if baby coming today. You go back home. Me midwife." I looked at the patient and she didn't make any reply, so I said to myself, "Well, women have been having their babies for a good many hundreds of years, farther back than we can count, without having a doctor. . . . "

But I learned a lesson that day. Several hours afterward, I was called back to Nyanza. I was there just in time to see the mother die, although the baby was born before that and was quite healthy. The mother had a retained placenta and the old midwife, getting over-anxious, pulled on the cord too hard, tore the cord, and there was considerable bleeding.

But it wasn't only the Indians who sometimes refused my services. I remember that a few years after the Nyanza incident, I was called in the middle of the night to a home of white people, about seven miles east of Baddeck, on a confinement case. The husband met me at the gate with a lantern and told me I could go back as the baby was already born. Remembering the mother's death in Nyanza, I said, "I am going in to see if the mother and baby are all right." He practically forbade me to go in, but I went anyway. I found that it was a breech birth; the child was born, all but the head, half an hour before I got there. I spent an hour that night before I got the baby breathing. The baby died the next day. Still, I felt rather relieved about that, as I am sure the child would have been mentally retarded had it lived.

I made many trips to the Indian village over the years and made many friends among the Micmacs. The lot of the Indians wasn't good in the early years. They were wards of the federal government, supported for the most part by rations paid for by the federal government and supplied by the local merchant. The politics of the merchant who got this business were always that of the government of the day.

The first year I provided medical services for Nyanza, I wrote the Department of Indian Affairs about the ration list. It didn't contain enough protein, and there was an abnormal amount of lard passed out to each family per month.

The Department answered that the ration list was made out by a competent dietitian. I presume the same list applied to all Indian villages across Canada. It was assumed that the Indians would get their protein by hunting and fishing, and the lard was to be used for cooking. I found out later that they weren't using as much lard as it appeared from the ration list: The Indians would buy strawberry jam or codfish or whatever else they wanted and it was charged up as lard.

The Indians supplemented their rations by making and selling ax-handles, butter tubs, and baskets; they sold a few eels in the spring and fall of the year and sometimes, in season, blueberries. They couldn't have been as well off as they were before the white man arrived in this country. They lived in wooden frame one-room houses, no matter how large the family. If they had more than one room they never used it. They had one bed, which was for the sick. When it wasn't in use for the sick, the young children would be put crossways in it to sleep. All the adults slept on the floor; they would take off their coats, roll them into pillows, and lie down on the floor, dressed almost as they were all day, with the fire, of course, going all night in the wintertime.

It was a hard life for them, and treating illnesses in an Indian home posed special problems. For one thing, you never knew what concoctions made of roots, bark, berries, or herbs had already been administered to the patient before the doctor was called in. There were motherly women who took infinite pleasure in making ointments, applying poultices, and preparing the most disagreeable potions.

I guess the worst of these concoctions I ever encountered was in 1934 when we had an epidemic of measles, a strain that was quite virulent, in many cases complicated by pneumonia. I had so many country calls, night and day, that I simply didn't have time to answer all of them. When I received a call to see Victor Pierro, then a boy of twelve, at Nyanza, it was three days before I could see him.

When I entered the house, his parents showed me a large kettle of evil-smelling liquid on the stove and told me they were giving Victor a glassful every two hours. "Gosh," I said, "that's great stuff. Give him lots of that." I thought to myself that it was just a tea made from herbs or roots of certain trees and bushes, which I knew the Indians used a great deal.

Happily, Victor had no complications, and I left some aspirin and some cough mixture for him. When I was about to leave, his father said to me, "Doctor, would you really like to know what is in this pot on the stove?"

I asked, "What is in it?"

The old chief said, "I tried to get you for three days and you didn't come, so I mixed up some of our own medicine."

Indeed he had! He had gone out into the pasture and gathered up enough sheep manure to more than half fill the pot. Then he had added water to fill it up and put it on the back of the stove until it began to simmer. Every two hours Victor had to drink a glassful.

I didn't tell them to stop using this special "tea," but perhaps the expression on my face conveyed the message. The next day I heard via the grapevine that Victor was much improved. I like to think the aspirin and cough mixture helped.

There have been tremendous changes in Indian life in my time. The business of selling ax-handles, butter tubs, and baskets disappeared with the changing times, and the Indian has had to compete in the labor market. This has been a slow and tedious process. Many of the younger men are skilled tradesmen and a few have gone in for higher education. Their education is paid for by the Department of Indian Affairs as far as they want to go, and in some cases have a better chance of changing their lot in life than many white children.

The greatest hurdle the Indian has to overcome is the notion that he is a second-class citizen. The advice to the Indian applies to any ethnic group. Let them cherish and honor their past, but look to the future and prepare themselves in their youth so they may progressively continue to contribute to society. Many are doing just that. The time may come sooner than we think when there will be no Department of Indian Affairs. I have faith that these people will eventually manage their own affairs.

There used to be a certain amount of rum smuggling in these parts—perhaps there still is. Rum runners would bring it in from St. Pierre and Miquelon and hide it on the shore in some remote area. On one occasion the rum was hidden right across St. Ann's Bay from Indian Brook, at a place called Beacha na Berrich (an anglicized Gaelic term meaning "dogfish beach.") It was a much stronger rum than was available in the liquor stores.

I found out about this special rum one cold morning at breakfast at Donnie Morrison's house in Wreck Cove. He had spent the night driving me over Smoky Mountain and back for a confinement case at Ingonish Harbour. It had been a hard night for us both, a difficult delivery for me and a bad night's driving for Donnie. The weather was stormy, the road almost impassable, and the sleigh had capsized more than once.

When we reached Donnie's home the next morning, we were tired and cold. His mother started getting breakfast for us, and Donnie asked whether I'd like a little hot rum toddy. I agreed that that would be a good idea; we needed it. And I still remember that it was the best toddy I've ever had.

Donnie told me the story of the rum. A couple of lobster fishermen from the Indian Brook area were tending their traps along the opposite shore. When they got thirsty and went ashore for drinking water, they came across this cache of rum—all kinds of it, so the story goes, in kegs and gallon cans. I don't know how many trips the fishermen made, but the story is that they nearly swamped their boat each trip, carrying the rum across to the Indian Brook side where they hid it. Some of the rum was sold or given to people living along the shore, but most of it was sold back to the original smugglers at five dollars a keg.

I remembered that story many times that winter and I remembered how good that hot toddy had been when we were half-frozen. And I wondered whether there might be some of that rum still available along the North Shore. So, sometime the following spring, I decided to find out. I made inquiries and was told, "You go see so-and-so. He might have some left." The man is dead and gone for years now, so I won't mention his name, but when I asked him about the rum, he said, "Well, I have one quart of that left. I wouldn't give it to anyone else, but I can't say no to you." He went outdoors and got a fork. His house had been banked for the winter with sod. He said, "It's time now this banking was taken down; spring is here." He started removing the banking from the side of the house and in under the sod, he turned up a bottle of this rum. I took it home and put it away.

A few months later, in July or August, I came home one night after a long day's work out in the country, arriving home about eleven. My wife was having a table of bridge. She wasn't playing herself, but Hannah was there, and Mrs. Jim, and two elderly maiden ladies who had no tolerance whatever for anybody who ever took a drink. I said to myself, "Hannah would love a drink and so would Mrs. Jim, but how am I going to give them a drink with those other two ladies at the same table?" I finally solved the problem.

I got out the glasses and filled two of them with grape juice. The others I half filled with white rum, and then filled them up with the grape juice. I gave the glasses to my wife to serve to her guests, carefully pointing out which glasses were for Hannah and Mrs. Jim and which were for the two maiden ladies. "Don't you get them mixed," I said.

The first indication that my wife might have mixed them up was that one of the maiden ladies began to talk a little more freely than was usual, a little bit louder, and she seemed to get the odd laugh in now and then. I began to wonder. The next indication was when Mrs. Jim came into the kitchen. "What do you think I am?" she asked. "You gave everybody a drink and you didn't give me one."

Nothing was said that night, but the incident worried me. The two ladies might think I had tried to pull a smart one by giving them a drink of liquor, three ounces or more, when they had probably never had a drink in their lives. It wasn't long after that when I was called to their home. Again I worried, but the incident wasn't mentioned. That mistake bothered me for years, even after they had both died. I stopped worrying about it recently when I heard that after the two of them had passed on it was found that all their stocks were in order, neatly packed in their safe deposit box—except for their stocks in *breweries*. These were found hidden in the bottom of a trunk, in the privacy of their home. Then I stopped worrying about the mistake.

When you go about collecting stories concerning a medical practice of more than forty years, I suppose you're bound to hear a few you had completely forgotten. Frank MacDonald of Washabuck had a couple that come in this category. This is the way he tells them: "I don't remember what year it was, but they were expecting a baby at Jimmy MacKenzie's. Dr. MacMillan was apparently a little worried about the case, because he told the Mackenzies that if they couldn't get him the first time they called the office, they should ask his wife to get in touch with him right away. The time came and they called the office. Mrs. MacMillan said the doctor had gone to the dentist in Sydney but that she'd call him.

"Dr. MacMillan was in the chair and the dentist was drilling when the call came. When the nurse said Dr. MacMillan was wanted at Jimmie MacKenzie's, the doctor took a jump out of the chair and broke the drill in two. He drove from Sydney by way of Grand Narrows ferry to Iona and arrived in Washabuck in time to deliver the baby. After it was over, he showed the part of the bit from the drill still in his tooth."

Frank had another story that seemed to indicate that I had moments of absent-mindedness—at least he must have laid it to absent-mindedness, because he went on being friendly. I had gone to Washabuck in the small motor boat and got Frank to drive me to Barra Glen where I had several calls to make. It was a fine day when we started out, but by the time the calls were completed a storm had come up. I went home with Frank for a bite to eat before taking the boat back to Baddeck. Frank takes up the story: "The storm was really bad. The doctor had on a nice cap, but not very warm. My mother was living then and she suggested that the doctor take my good leather cap. He took it and went down to the shore and got the boat back to Baddeck. I waited and waited to get my leather cap back, but that leather cap was just not coming back. The cap was a year old but it was still good, and I needed a warm cap. So I sent to Eaton's for another one, the same kind.

"Shortly after I got my new cap, I got another call from Dr. MacMillan to meet him at MacKay's Point and drive him to see a patient. When he got off the boat what did I see but my cap on his head. He made his call and on the way back he called in at our place for a cup of tea. Later I drove him to the boat. I came home and went to put my cap on before going to the barn, and there was my old one, the one he had been wearing for months. He'd taken my new cap." Apparently I was completely unaware of Frank's problem and wondering where in the world I had acquired the new cap.

I'm afraid I wasn't always as tactful as I should have been in my comments to patients. More than once I spoke quickly before I really thought about what I was going to say, and then wished I hadn't said it. Maybe the worst of those pop-offs was when I was treating Frank MacGregor of Nyanza.

During the latter part of the 1950s, Frank began to complain of some soreness and pain in his chest when he exerted himself at work. I advised him to walk slowly and stop frequently for little rests while walking. I gave him nitroglycerine tablets to put under his tongue if the pain didn't ease up as soon as he stopped walking. This went on, intermittently, for a few years. On one or two occasions we had him in the hospital for a short period with a diagnosis of suspected coronary ischemia.

On May 12, 1959, about eight-thirty in the morning, Frank was standing by the roadside near his own gate, waiting for the school bus on which he very often came in to Baddeck. Just as the bus stopped for him, he took a severe pain in his chest, different and much worse than any pain he had ever had before. The bus driver heard him groan, noticed his color and limp condition, and drove him right to my office before taking the children to school. I wasn't there at the time, but Millie MacLeod, a trained nurse who was working in my office then, located me directly and I was there within a few minutes. My diagnosis then, from clinical evidence, was that Frank had suffered a heavy coronary infarction. We moved Frank to the hospital and got him into bed. He had another massive attack about this time. We put him in the oxygen tent, one arm out through the zipper of the tent so we could administer intravenous drugs and take his blood pressure frequently.

When we first took him in, he had a systolic blood pressure of approximately 180. Then it began to drop. I was taking it frequently. From 180 it went down to 170, down to 160, then on down to 60. By this time I was giving him everything but the proverbial kitchen sink to try to keep his pressure up.

It went down to 40. He was in a cold sweat, worrying, afraid he was going to die. He said, "Doctor, did you ever see them go any lower than that?" "Lots of them," I said.

Then Frank asked, "Doctor, what happened to those people whose pressure went lower than this?"

And I answered, obviously without stopping to think about it, "Every damn one of them died!"

It wasn't a very sensible remark for me to make right then. I said it so quickly that Frank began to laugh, as sick as he was. He told me afterwards that he reasoned, "Well, heck, I'm probably going to die but I'm not the first man to die. I've seen my day." And he stopped worrying and his pressure began to go up. Perhaps the remark did him as much good as all the drugs I pumped into him during that short period to keep his pressure from falling to fatal level. Frank was in the hospital about a month and left in good condition. He lived almost another ten years. And then it wasn't the heart condition that caused his death. One morning as he walked to his mail box, he was struck by a car.

Another case of my foot-in-mouth habit concerned Dr. Bob Cox, a retired doctor who lived in Nyanza. He had retired early in life because of post-coronary heart syndrome. One day in 1961, he was mixing mortar for the stone chimney he was building for his fireplace, when he suddenly developed a severe pain in the chest and went into shock.

I was at home when the call came and I was with him just a very few minutes later. The evidence was plain enough: he had had another major coronary infarction. I gave him a third of a grain of morphine and waited twenty minutes for it to take effect. Then I put him in the back seat of my car and started for the Baddeck hospital.

I took people with heart attacks into the hospital many times. Once I had started, I'd never look back to see how they were. When they were quiet I was always afraid that something had gone wrong, but I couldn't do much about it anyway. I'd just press harder on the gas pedal and keep on driving.

Apparently that was my frame of mind on that day, and here's how Dr. Bob recalls that trip: "By this time the sedation had worked a fair amount, and driving along the road to Baddeck, along the Bras d'Or Lake, it was a beautiful evening with fresh air coming in. The fresh air seemed to be a great help in alleviating the pressure in my chest. But everything seemed very quiet. We were going along and I remarked to you, 'It would be a nice evening to be out on the lake spearing eels.' You came back with a very quick retort, with a little of your stammering you occasionally do, and said, 'Ah-ah-ah-ah, I'm glad you said something: I thought you were dead.'"

Maybe treating heart patients loosens up my tongue for some reason. I made a similar slip once when I was taking a cardiogram. This time there were two other doctors involved.

I was taking care of Dr. Walter Myers, who was spending the summer in his home at Baddeck Bay. Dr. Myers was a cardiologist who practiced in Washington, D.C. I took my electrocardiograph machine down to his house to take a heart tracing; en route, I picked up Dr. Fraser Nicholson, who was home for the weekend, and asked him to help me. Here is Dr. Nicholson's recollection of the incident:

"Dr. MacMillan came down to my place and asked me to go with him to Walter's, next door, to take a cardiograph. Walter was resting in his studio, a little cottage over in the woods beyond the pond. The machine we were using was a battery-operated one, so there no problem about cutting off the power, and we didn't anticipate any trouble with the tracing. However, we had great difficulty in getting the galvanometer zeroed. We finally discovered that Walt had an electric sheet on the bed and its wires had set up a field which was interfering. We got rid of this, got everything zeroed and started to run the electrocardiograph.

"Walt was very interested in this and, of course, as a cardiologist he was keenly aware of all our procedures. In fact, he even helped. Dr. MacMillan was doing the chest leads and Walt was holding the chest electrodes. We had put some cardio paste on his chest and it was pretty greasy. Doc was watching the needle on the galvanometer, and suddenly the tracing became just a straight line. He looked up quickly, swung his head over to Walt, then back to the tracing. 'Good God, Walt, I thought you were dead,' he exclaimed. What had happened was that the chest electrode which Walt was holding had slipped right off the chest to the side. Walt and I just had convulsions from laughing. It was five minutes before we could continue taking the cardiograph."

Over the years I called on Dr. Myers many times for help during his summer vacations in Baddeck. He was always very obliging and taught me a great deal. In addition to being a cardiologist, he was a specialist in internal medicine, and of course having his practice in Washington enabled him to keep right up to date on medical advances.

One time I called on him for assistance was on August 13, 1955, the day of the official opening of the Canso Causeway, the engineering feat that annexes the mainland of Nova Scotia to Cape Breton Island. I was anxious to attend the ceremony, but worried about being away from Baddeck for a few hours because I had no one to cover for me.

I suppose I had a special interest in the causeway because I was a member of the Legislative Assembly of the province and had lived through the many arguments about it. Like any major project undertaken by any government, this causeway was criticized by a number of citizens while it was being constructed. The critics said it couldn't be done. This was great ammunition for the local bards, who eulogized the project by poem and song using the term, "The Bochan Bridge of Canso."

I was up early that morning, made my rounds in the hospital and made a few calls in town. By mid-morning everything was quiet and peaceful. My wife was all ready for the trip, fuming because up to this point I had not said whether or not I would be able to go. Finally I decided to go, and once I had made up my mind, we weren't long in getting on the road. The ribbon was to be cut at two o'clock.

When we arrived at the Strait, I picked a parking spot where I could make a quick getaway, if necessary. Before we had time to get out of the car, I was hopelessly jammed in on all sides by other cars. There would be no way in the world for me to move my car until the party was all over.

Before going to the ceremony I went to a telephone and called the hospital to let them know my predicament. And I was told that Mrs. Aloysius MacKinnon from Iona Rear had just arrived at the hospital, in labor, with pains every five minutes.

I was in trouble. There was no way I could get my car out. I thought first of trying to get a taxi, but realized this would be impossible on that day with the greatest event of the century taking place in that area. I just sat there for three or four minutes, trying to find a solution. I abruptly went to the telephone again and called Dr. Myers and explained the situation. I waited another twenty minutes and called the hospital again. The nurse on duty told me that both Dr. Myers and Dr. Jarmen were there, taking care of my patient. Dr. Dabney Jarmen, also from Washington, D.C., was a urologist. He, too, had a summer home near Baddeck and he, too, helped me many times.

The doctors told me afterward that neither one of them had attended a delivery since their intern years. But they had a perfect patient and everything went along well. The baby was born shortly before two o'clock. The doctors watched the clock on the wall, and exactly at two, just as the ribbon was being cut on the causeway, they cut the cord!

When I arrived home that night, I went to the hospital. Mrs. MacKinnon liked the doctors so well that she wanted to name the new baby girl for both of them. I coined the name for the baby: Jarmine Myra. The mother added another, so the baby's full name was Jarmine Myra Regina MacKinnon.

Dr. Myers was married to a granddaughter of Professor Alexander Graham Bell. His mother-in-law was a daughter of Graham Bell and the wife of Dr. Gilbert Grosvenor. Over the years I was the family physician to many of Bell's descendants. Many spent their summers at Beinn Breagh on what was the Bell estate, where the old home still stands on a point overlooking the Bras d'Or Lakes.

I like to think about a very pleasant trip I had in 1962—much different from those I have described here.

By 1962 Dr. and Mrs. Grosvenor had reached an age and state of health when traveling from their home in Baddeck to their winter home in Florida was a problem. That year they decided to charter a plane that they used frequently in *National Geographic* work, and asked me to fly with them to Miami. As their family physician, it was my responsibility, when approaching Washington, to decide whether they were too tired, or not well enough, to fly on to Miami. If I decided they weren't well enough, I was to give the order to land at the airport in Washington. I must admit that Miami in November (it was the 22nd) sounded good to me. What influence this had on my decision to continue to Miami, I cannot say.

In any event, it was a good flight, non-stop for nine hours and twenty-five minutes from the Sydney airport to the one in Miami. We played bridge most of the time, stopping now and then while the two patients rested, and they arrived home none the worse for the trip.

The contrast between some of my early trips, with patients wrapped in blankets and carried in hay-filled sleighs through long hours of below-zero weather, and this one, high above the clouds in great ease and comfort, is a good measure of the change that came about during my years of practice.

14

"PHYSICIAN, HEAL THYSELF ..."

For most of my years of practice, I was blessed with excellent health. Or perhaps I was just too busy to notice when I was sick. But there were a few times when I had to give up and go to bed. This was a serious matter, because there was no other doctor available, either to take care of me or of the other sick people in my area.

One summer night in the early 1930's, my family was away and I was home alone. Perhaps because of being overtired, during the evening I became very sick, with chills and vomiting. I took some medication, got myself quieted and went to bed.

I'd been asleep two or three hours when I awoke to find a sailor standing alongside the bed and shaking me. Stationed on one of the ships in Baddeck that summer, he was now in great agony, with severe pain in his abdomen. He had not been able to pass water for more than twenty-four hours. With a few questions and a little examination, I found he had a phimosis of the foreskin.

We had no hospital here then, nor was there any other doctor. I was still shivering and shaking, too sick to go downstairs to my office. So I sent him down, told him where to find certain instruments I would need, and where I kept the local anesthesia. This was before we had electricity in the village, so I gave him directions for stirring up the fire in the kitchen range and putting the instruments on to boil.

All this he did, despite his acute discomfort. In about twenty minutes time he came back upstairs with the tray of sterile instruments, needles, syringes, scissors, artery forceps, etc. I was barely able to get as far as the washroom to scrub up, and then I sat on the edge of the bed. The sailor stood alongside me, and I did what we call a "dorsal slit." I think I had to put in only one or two sutures and he was able to go to the bathroom then and relieve himself.

I never saw the sailor afterwards. I don't believe I even asked him his name; I was feeling too sick to take any records or make any notes in the book.

Another time I was ill may have been the result of tension, over-exertion, and eating unwisely and too well. On the morning of the first day of April, 1931, there were three calls within a very few minutes, all in the same direction. The first was to go to Murdoch (Rob) MacLeod's house at South Gut. There I would be met by Murdoch Campbell from Englishtown with his daughter, who had a broken arm. There was also a call to go to Tarbot to see Mrs. Rhoda Carmichael, and a call to Peter Briggette's out in North River Meadow.

I went to the barn, gave the mare a feed, came back and had a cup of coffee, and packed my bags. By this time Gypsy Queen was through her breakfast and we started out. It was during spring break-up, and the first four miles the road was bare of snow. I used a two-wheeled sulky and changed to a sleigh at Kennie MacRitchi's at Baddeck Bay. By noon I had arrived at South Gut, just in time for dinner—pickled codfish with pork scraps, turnip, and potato. Not having taken time for breakfast before starting out that morning, I was certainly hungry. But no sooner had I started to eat when Mr. and Mrs. Campbell and their daughter came in, so I rushed through the meal.

The Campbells had had a bad trip. The road was completely impassable, even for a horse and sleigh. Everyone had used the ice all winter, and the road hadn't been broken through yet. But now the ice was so poor that Murdoch had been afraid to drive on it, and had traveled instead along the shoreline on the sea wall. Many times he had had to jump out and steady the sleigh when the horse was jumping clampers. The seven-mile trip had taken them three hours.

The daughter had broken her arm three weeks previously; they had known it was broken because the bones made a noise every time the arm moved. It was only after the swelling cleared up that they realized how crooked it was, and decided they had better have me set it. I had to put the patient to sleep with chloroform, break the fracture again, and straighten the arm. It was never x-rayed. They started back for Englishtown, with the girl's arm in a plaster cast. It was probably an uncomfortable trip for her.

I set out for my next call at Tarbot, fourteen miles away. I knew the road over the North Gut hills was just step-holes in the snow. If I could only get across the ice on St. Ann's Harbour, I would save three or four hours. The temptation was so great, I succumbed.

For the first half-mile the ice seemed good, except that the mare did not want to trot and seemed to be testing every step. Then suddenly, both front feet went through the ice. Before I had time to think, she was out. In the next mile or more she put either one or two feet through the ice about fifty times. If it had been four feet at once, that would have been it. We were both in a sweat; the pickled codfish and pork scraps I had had for lunch felt like a football in my stomach—and a very heavy football at that. We were both glad to get ashore at Murray and I was at my second call for the day at about five o'clock.

I can't remember what illness there was that day at Mrs. Carmichael's. I prescribed what I thought was necessary, if I had it with me. Or if I didn't have exactly what I wanted, I used the next best. In any event, whatever I used must have been all right because she lived for nearly thirty years after that. I ate supper there—two fried eggs and ham, which I put down in a minute or two because I was anxious to get on the road again to see the next patient.

I turned back to North River and then drove out to the Meadow and reached Peter Briggette's at ten o'clock at night. I forget who was sick, but again I had a meal before I left, even though I could still taste the pickled codfish.

Now the problem was to get home. I dreaded the trip around North Gut Hills. It was a very frosty night, and I was sure I could safely go back the same way I came, but Gypsy Queen thought differently. When I got on the ice at Murray, she cut across the mouth of North River and went ashore at Munroe's Point. She just refused to head out on St. Ann's Harbour ice.

So we had to take the long way around. The mare would have to take her feet out of one-step-hole and reach for the next. It was a long slow trip. I was hours getting around North Gut. Somewhere along the route I fell sound asleep in the sleigh. When I woke up I was in chills, with pains in my stomach and vomiting. One can only take so much tension—and the food had been so good!

I reached Kennie MacRitchie's at Baddeck Bay about daylight. There was no one up there, but I left their sleigh and changed to my sulky. I got home and went to bed where I stayed for two weeks. It was absolutely impossible for me to get up, regardless of how sick anybody was. I ran a temperature of 102 degrees and 103 degrees for a week or so, and then gradually began to get better.

On October 13, 1950, I wasn't feeling well. I continued working for a while, but when I took my temperature and found it was 104 degrees, I admitted myself to the hospital. I was there as a patient until November 7. I thought at first that I'd be ill only a few days, so I didn't try to get anyone to fill in for me. About a week later, I tried, only to find it was impossible. I don't think I had any doctor come to see me at the time. Our x-rays suggested that I might have had a straight virus infection in the chest, but that was as near as we came to a diagnosis.

When I was first confined to the hospital, I made a round of patients, and anyone who was able to leave the hospital was discharged. We still had thirteen patients left and the number in the hospital never went below this during the period I was confined. Once each day I got up, put on bathrobe and slippers, and made a round of those who were there. We spread the word throughout the area that any emergencies, or anyone who felt he must see a doctor right away, should go into North Sydney, Sydney, or Inverness. Even so, I was caught in the hospital with a few emergencies to attend to.

During the first week I was there, while I was still carrying a temperature of 104 degrees, an accident case arrived. The accident had occurred quite near Baddeck, so naturally they headed for our hospital. One woman was badly hurt. I believe I had to do some suturing. Besides this, she had a Colles fracture of the left wrist with a very marked deformity. For this I had to give a complete chloroform anesthesia and then set the wrist. I believe I did the best job that night that I ever did on a Colles fracture, with perfect results.

During that same week, while I was still carrying a temperature of 104 degrees, a maternity case arrived in the hospital. The people concerned weren't aware that I was ill, although we had tried to circulate the message through the country that these cases were to go to another hospital.

The patient was in a very heavy labor when she arrived, so I couldn't send her on to another hospital. I got up and delivered the baby. It was an instrument delivery, which wasn't too serious. The complication was that she had a retained placenta that I could not express, no matter how hard I tried. The delivery of the placenta was urgent; I knew the patient couldn't stand the profuse bleeding for too many minutes.

I had to give her a complete chloroform anesthesia and with the left hand over the fundus, using the right hand and arm, I had to go in and separate the placenta from the uterine wall. The mother and baby did fine, but the nurses told me later that they thought for sure, from my color, that I was going to go under the table before I was through.

The remainder of the time I spent in the hospital was uneventful enough, but after I began to feel a little better, I had a steady stream of patients to my bedside in the hospital. Although I was still running an afternoon temperature of 100 degrees, by November 7 I decided that it would be easier on me if I were home rather than seeing so many patients at my bedside. It took a month before my temperature levelled off and came down to normal.

When I left the hospital, I didn't go right home, but drove down to West Tarbot to see a five-year-old boy, Angus Smith, son of D. J. Smith. His parents had brought him in to see me about a week before, while I was in the hospital. He had a cold in his chest, a temperature, decreased breath sounds, and dullness in the base of both lungs. The diagnosis was pneumonia and I started him on antibiotics. Just before I left the hospital I got word he was having pain and soreness in the abdomen. When I got to his home in West Tarbot, twenty-five miles or more from Baddeck, I found he had a ruptured appendix and I immediately sent him to North Sydney Hospital. He had surgery with good recovery.

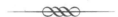

By 1962 my son had finished medical school and entered practice with me in Baddeck. On December 3, 1964, at nine o'clock in the morning, I was in my office getting ready to go to Middle River on a medical call. My son was doing the hospital work that morning. While I was packing my bags, I suddenly developed a severe pain in my chest. That was it—a heart attack. I spent several weeks in the hospital and didn't return to work for a year and a half.

In May of 1966 I decided to do a small practice from my old office in the house, trying to keep the work down to two or three hours a day. That didn't work very well, and it wasn't long before I was working twenty hours a day again. I was so happy being back at work that I didn't count the hours.

In trying to keep stress and strain to a minimum during that period, I would take my time if I had a country call. Very often I'd stop and see some old friends along the road. On the afternoon of August 12, 1966, returning from Iona through Cain's Mountain, I decided to stop and see Christine MacIvor, who lived there with her sister, Etta. I opened the door and walked in. No one seemed to be home. The fire was burning in the kitchen stove. The dinner was sitting there on the stove, all dried out. I looked around and then I saw a pair of feet sticking out through the pantry doorway.

"Physician, Heal Thyself..."

Christine was on the floor, completely unconscious, deathly white and gray, covered with a cold sweat. Her clothes were wet through and through from perspiration. Christine was a diabetic. I knew it must be an insulin reaction and from the fact that the dinner was still on the stove, I knew that she had been there for at least four hours.

In my bag I kept a 50 c.c. vial of a 50 per cent glucose solution, just for this type of emergency. I was sure Christine had only a few more minutes of life unless I could get part of that vial of sugar solution into one of her veins. First I had to stir up the fire, boil a syringe, fill it with the solution, and then with luck I found a vein and pushed 20 c.c. of the solution into the bloodstream. With that, she sat up and looked at me. Then she started to laugh. "Where on earth did you come from?" she asked. She went upstairs, changed her clothes, and then came down and we had some lunch. Later she got dressed up and went to a wedding at Little Narrows.

When I first found her unconscious, I felt a tight, constrictive pain across my chest, which kept getting worse until I finally got the needle into her vein. However, as soon as she regained consciousness, I relaxed, and the tightness and distress in my chest gradually eased.

Just a few weeks later, on the 18th of September, 1966, about two or three in the morning, I woke with another pain in my chest. That was the finale as far as my medical practice went.

FIRST THINGS LAST

*D*uring the very busy years of my practice, it sometimes seemed to me that I didn't even have time to think. But there were other times, as I sat behind the horse on fine starlit nights, that my mind would wander, taking me back to my life as a boy in the village of Goldboro, Guysborough County, Nova Scotia, where I was born in 1903, up through the years of high school, university, and then the problems of settling into medical practice on Cape Breton Island.

I often pondered the various events and circumstances that led along the paths and eventually brought me to this part of the world. I had been brought up in a religion that did not preach predestination but left one with an open mind, and so I often thought about the course my life had taken, and why and how.

I was eleven years of age when World War One broke out. The shortage of manpower in the country made it very easy for a boy to drop out of school, and like many of my friends, I did just that. I worked four years on a fish wharf, ten to fifteen hours a day, eight months of the year. Of necessity in the winter I went to the woods to cut, haul, saw, and split twenty cords of wood, our year's supply of fuel. In my spare time, which would be two to three months a year, I attended school, but never graded any year.

It was during these war years that I decided what I wanted to do in life, but in the fall of 1918 we had no school teacher in our area and didn't get one until February 1919. What records she fell heir to, I don't know, but I told her I was in grade nine, and she took my word for it.

The teacher was a Cape Bretoner, a Miss Mary MacLeod of Orangedale. She was an excellent teacher and dedicated to her work. I remember one evening I took an hour off from study and rowed across the harbor to the ice cream parlor on the Isaac's Harbor side. I was quite embarrassed when I walked in and saw the teacher there. I heard about it in school the next day. I'm sure it was her help and encouragement that kept me going so that I was able to pass the grade nine provincial examinations in June. If I hadn't passed, that would have been it as far as further education was concerned.

In the following years, I finished grades ten and eleven at Sydney Academy, working during the summer months. Then I went off to the university, but returned for summer work in Sydney until my final year, when I interned at the Victoria General Hospital in Halifax.

With all the millions of dollars both the provincial and federal governments have put up these last few years for education, it is still more costly to the student today than it was when I went to college. I was able to earn enough in the summer to pay my own tuition and buy my own books and my own clothes. This left my father with my board to pay—one dollar per day. He used to send me thirty-five dollars every month to cover my board, laundry, and spending money. That meant just a dollar or two a month for spending money, but I still had a good time. Most of my classmates were in the same boat. Our parties were simpler than the parties they have today.

I have already recounted how I came to Baddeck in August 1928, having graduated in Medicine from Dalhousie University that May and spent the summer doing a *locum tenens* in Lunenburg County.

My early years in Baddeck were called "The Hungry Thirties." The depression was world-wide. Victoria County was never an industrial area, and the people were still living off the land. Even in the village some people had their own pigs, cows, and hens, and tilled the soil for planting. Victoria County never enjoyed boom times, but during those years neither did it become as economically depressed as the industrial areas.

During these years I ate in every home in the county. I would look the table over. Meat, vegetables, fish, milk, eggs, butter, home-baked breads and cakes were all there. These were the products of their own labor. I've since eaten in the best restaurants across Canada and the United States, and I've never found any better meals than those prepared in the homes here during that era. Some might argue that they brought out the very best for the doctor, but this was not always so. It was my custom at mealtime to turn my horse in at the nearest home. I was often unexpected, but I was always welcome and never disappointed in the fare.

At that time, many Cape Bretoners were employed in the lumber camps. A man worked from daylight until dark and earned twenty-five dollars per month, plus board. Those who looked after the horses were paid an additional five dollars a month. Lobster fishermen in the shore areas received three cents per pound for their lobsters. The very best of two-year-old beef at times was as low as three cents per pound by the carcass. Other produce was correspondingly low. Even in the professions, income was in proportion to the amount of money in the area. The cash income of most of the families in the county of Victoria was between three and five hundred dollars a year, and it took long hours of hard work to produce that.

It was a hard life for a doctor, too, but I enjoyed every minute of it. Once again I want to pay tribute to my wife Ethelean. Granted the new house we built in 1930 provided many conveniences that most country homes of that period lacked, but the life of a doctor's wife was not an easy one. She rarely knew when there would be extra people at the dinner table or when I would keep a patient in our home overnight. Countless times patients would arrive to see me when I was off at the other end of the county, and she had to deal with whatever the problem was until I could be reached. She had to cope with the problems of running a home and bringing up two lively children, often without my help for several days at a time. Possibly the greatest burden she bore, always uncomplainingly, was the knowledge that when I took off in bad storms or when the ice was soft on the lake, my chances for coming back were not necessarily good.

Our children, too, shared in the problems of a country medical practice. Without my family's support and understanding, whatever I may have contributed to the people I served would have been impossible.

I've never forgotten one lesson our son Monty taught me. When he was a small boy, probably two or three years of age, I took him with me on a call to Philip MacLean's at Upper Baddeck River, thirteen miles away. It was in the spring of the year, before the roads were healed. En route I stopped at the post office to pick up my mail, which I tossed on the seat of the car and forgot about. Among other things, the mail contained an assortment of pill samples.

When I had completed my house call, I returned to the car to find that the child had investigated the mail, as children will. I was horrified to discover that he had his mouth full of a number of pills that I knew contained strychnine. I had no idea how many he might have swallowed.

I turned the car around to get back to Baddeck as quickly as possible to get a stomach pump, but in my panic and excitement of the moment, I got the car stuck in the mud. I rushed him into the house I had just left and managed to get his stomach flushed out several times by making him drink water, then turning him upside down and putting my finger down his throat until he vomited. I repeated this about twelve times until he said, "Daddy, no more."

This episode made me realize and vividly brought home to me the fear and panic that occurs in a family miles away in the country, with no telephone and bad roads, when they are suddenly and unexpectedly faced with sickness in the family. I thought of this incident many times when I got calls at night at the height of a severe storm, or when there was unsafe ice to cross.

As a young girl my daughter Connie would walk the ice to Washabuck with me, carrying my bags, and she now says she can still remember how heavy those bags would become before we reached the top of the hill on the other side. When she became older she would drive me anywhere and at all hours while I slept in the back seat, and then she would patiently wait to drive me back home. Her enthusiasm, warmth, and good companionship were constant.

And, of course, as she helped me from an early age, so did my son Monty, who is a few years younger than Connie. Monty graduated from medical school as I was starting to "slow up," then came home to enter into practice with me. When I could no longer carry on, he was able to go back to school to specialize in radiology. How fortunate I am, and have been, in my family.

When sitting by the fireplace now, during the winter storms, I have my nostalgic moments. I often think back to those long, peaceful, starlit rides through this beautiful country. I remember how I would try to use that time to solve some of my problems of the day, to put things in their perspective. That was when I developed a philosophy of life that not only sustained me, but one that I could, perhaps unknowingly, pass on to those of my patients who were having what appeared to them to be insoluble difficulties. The best medicine was not always tangible.

Early retirement from work, even though it is a forced retirement for reasons of health, can be rewarding. The initial shock is pretty grim. I got a great deal of help by recalling the many times I sat in my office and counselled men who had the same problem. They would say to me, "Doctor, when I was working I thought the little world around me would come to an end if I couldn't play my part. Now when I wake up in the morning and realize the community is still functioning normally, there is a tendency to slip into the past, which I know is not healthy."

I agree that living solely in the past is not healthy, but one's life in the present is a merger of the past with the future, and both parts are necessary for a satisfying present.

My first immediate problem when I had recovered my health was to face the fact that I could not return to my medical practice. I then began to raise my tolerance for exercise by a graduated program of walking and gymnastics. At first my walks were only across the street and back, with a short rest on the other side. It took several months to progress to the point where I could walk four or five miles a day. At about this stage I found walking without a purpose other than exercise a little dull. I did some fishing that year, in season. The day I hooked a four-pound speckled trout with a dark Montreal fly, I was very pleased, but before I landed it I was not so sure fishing was the best thing for me.

Then I began to collect these stories. I enjoyed traveling around the county, reminiscing with so many old friends, having some laughs with them (and some nostalgic moments, too), and having a cup of tea.

One day one of my friends remarked, "Doctor, if you had made a fortune here during your practice, which I know you didn't, it wouldn't begin to compensate for all you endured."

My reply was, "I enjoyed every minute of it, and I'd do it all over again. I wouldn't change anything." The rewards have been great. If my readers enjoy perusing this story as much as I did in getting it together and writing it, that will be recompense enough.

So part of my retirement activity has been concerned with the past. Another part extends into the future. In 1966 I staked several square miles of land in the mountains, filing claims with the Department of Mines of Nova Scotia. I have become a prospector, with a valid prospector's license for each square mile. Since then I've been spending several hours a day, four or five days a week when the weather permits, alone in the mountains. I find it very relaxing, with no hurry and no worry. Sometimes I take a friend along for the day in the deep woods, but very few would go back a second time. It is rough country, up hill and down. The mountains are as high as 1,400 feet above sea level and with a grade of 37 degrees. One of my properties is the site of an old gold mine on Second Gold Brook in the Middle River area.

Many of my friends say to me, "Don't you think it's a bit risky for you to go away back in the mountains alone?"

"Yes," I reply, "but a calculated risk." A good compass and a knowledge of the maps of the area are essential.

In the deep woods, alone, the mind does wander back a bit into the past. At the same time the prospector's dream beckons one into the future. I have not yet found the pot of gold at the end of the rainbow deep in the woods, but a whole new interesting world has been opened to me.

And there is no pot of gold in the world that I would exchange for the one that gleams so brightly when I sit in front of an open fire with my good wife, our children and grandchildren (Kimberly, Jennifer, Kier, and Ian, all MacMillans). I like to think back to the happy moments in the past, and I look forward with faith to the future.

When I think about the numerous occasions I went into houses, even in the small hours of the morning, and never found a locked door or a family unwilling to help me, I know how fortunate I was to have made my choice of serving in this area. No one could find finer people, nor a lovelier spot in any country, than we have in this part of Cape Breton.